CW00740518

SELF-PROPAGATING

# Trees and Shrubs
# of Greece

By

## GEORGE SFIKAS

With 400 illustrations in colour
by the Author

**ISBN 960 226 072 6**

Reprinted 1990

Distributed by:
EFSTATHIADIS GROUP S.A.
Ag. Athanasiou Str. GR. 145 65 Anixi Attikis Tel. 8136871-2
14 Valtetsiou St. GR 106 80 Athens Tel. 3615011
34 Olympou-Diikitiriou St. GR. 546 30 Thessaloniki Tel. 511781

**EFSTATHIADIS** GROUP
Bookshop: 84 Academias St. Tel. 3637439

# CONTENTS

*Except where specifically shown, the scale of all the drawings is two and a half times less than actual size.*

5

# INTRODUCTION

Of all the European countries, Greece has the lowest percentage of forested land, about 85 per cent of its ground surface being bare of trees. This is an area made up of scrubland (*maquis*), fields and pasturage, as well as land completely barren and eroded.

This barrenness is not natural, but the result of man's long-term effect on his environment. One would naturally expect to find the whole of the Greek peninsula, with the exception of the highest mountain peaks, to be covered in woodland, and a few thousand years ago Greece was indeed covered with extensive forests though the climate then was in no way different from what it is now.

The trees making up these forests were exactly the same in ancient as in modern times: species characteristic of the Mediterranean and European countries. Their destruction began at the close of the Neolithic age, when man first built permanent dwellings and settled down to agriculture and husbandry. The forests of the plains had little by little to give way to fields and pasture land, and those on the sub-alpine mountain slopes (1,700 m - 2,200 m) suffered serious destruction at the hands of the new farmers, who burnt them down to convert them into extensive tracts for grazing.

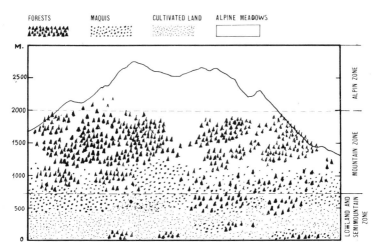

*Typical vegetation in the Greek highland zone.*

This practice, which began 6,000 years ago, has continued relentlessly ever since and is still continuing even today, though illegally. Nowadays, new hazards to the forests have joined the old: attempts at housing developments in wooded areas bordering the towns, and negligently started forest fires which are becoming distressingly more frequent.

Even so the tremendous regenerative power which is so distinctive a feature of the Greek flora would be capable of repairing at least part of the damage if the burnt-down areas were only left alone and not used for building-land or the grazing of goats. In many mountain areas which in the course of the last generation were almost completely abandoned by the local population, new forests have grown up to cover large expanses which had formerly been fields and pasture land. This does not, however, imply a generally brighter future for the Greek forests, since whatever improvement may occur in some areas is more than offset by the furious pace of continuing ravages in others. Every summer the forest fires are so many and extensive that it is impossible for the damage to be made good by the valiant effort at reforesting attempted by the authorities, whose means are very limited. As a consequence, the overall result remains negative, and a lot more must happen before the decline in Greece's forests can be halted and the trend reversed.

The greater part of the country's wooded land today is to be found at intermediate altitudes, on the flanks of the larger mountain ranges. This is explained by the fact that these relatively steep slopes are as unsuitable for cultivation as they are for grazing, and so have remained more or less untouched.

The most extensive forest stands are in northern Greece, in the mountains of Thrace, Macedonia and Epiros, but in central Greece too elevated rural areas are fairly well covered with conifers. In the Peloponnese, wooded land is very limited, and in Crete and on most of the Aegean islands it is deperately restricted. The islands in the northern and eastern Aegean, and similarly those of the Ionian sea, are to a large extent covered with pines as well as other forest trees.

Certain types of tree which in ancient times used to be plentiful in the huge evergreen forests of the plains are today found only sporadically on the boundaries between fields, or in small clumps in odd corners. They include various species of oak trees, such as *quercus aegilops.* Subalpine species, such as *pinus heldreichii* or the wild cypress *(juniperus foetidissima),* whose natural habitat was destroyed to become pasture land, suffered similar depredation.

However, poor as today's Greece may be in forest vegetation, it is still rich in the variety of species. The country as a whole has over 200 species of tree and large shrub, and it is these which form the content of this book.

The greater part of the Greek forests consists of conifers, with deciduous trees such as beeches and chestnuts coming second. The other species grow rather sporadically here and there in the forests, on scrubland or in fields, and are rarely found in extensive or homogeneous stands.

The Greek forests can be roughly divided into three categories, according to the predominant species:

(a) deciduous highland forests in the north, consisting of beeches, either by themselves or mixed in with other deciduous trees;

(b) coniferous highland forests throughout Greece, made up of different species of pine and fir;

*Geographical map of Greece.*

(c) mediterranean forests on the lower mountain slopes, where Aleppo pine is by far the most common, often mingling with needled conifers, kerm-oak, holm-oak, ash, and various species of shrub.

Most of the trees of Greece are types common to all of Europe. However, there are also some Asian species - such as *juniperus drupacea* and *fagus moesiaca* - which do not exist in other European countries. Certain endemics, such as *abies cephalonica, phoenix theophrastii,* and *abelicea cretica,* can also be found.

It is worth noting here that Greece today has several trees and shrubs which, though they originated in other countries, have become very common in certain regions and have acclimatised themselves so well that they grow like native species. Characteristic examples are the very widespread Tree of Heaven *(ailanthus altissimus)* with its large feathery leaves, which originally came to Greece from Asia, as did the fig tree *(ficus carica):* species from America are the yellow tubular-flowered *nicotina glauca,* and the acacia *(robinia pseudacia).*

*Black Pines in Pieria mountains in Macedonia.*

*Scots Pines in Valia Kalda in the Pindus mountains.*

*Black Pines in the Taygetus range in the Peloponnese.*

Balkan Pines on Mt Olympus, where they easily grow at heights of up to 2,400 meters.

*Mixed deciduous trees in the valley of the Aoos river, in Epirus.*

*European Beeches in the foreground, Black Pines on Mt Olympus behind.*

*Moisture-loving trees by the river Voidomatis in the Pindus range, with deciduous trees on the mountain slopes beyond.*

15

*Many Greek mountains have been completely denuded of trees, such as Mt Siniatsiko in Western Macedonia, one of the most barren areas in the whole country.*

*Mixed forest in the eastern Pindus range (Mt Lingos), consisting of Macedonian Fir and European Beech.*

*European Beeches in the Pieria mountains.*

*Flowering shrubs in the **maquis** on Skyros island.*

17

# IDENTIFICATION OF SPECIMENS BY MEANS OF LEAVES

The flowers of a tree or shrub are of course one of the easiest means for identifying at least the genus if not the actual species. However, the flowers last only a very short time, at the very most for four weeks. The fruits too, though they may remain on the plant somewhat longer, are not found at all times of the year, and are thus equally unreliable for purposes of identification.

The leaves on the other hand remain on the branches for at least 7-8 months at a time, even in the case of deciduous trees, and are therefore the best aid to identification. Examination of the leafy branch, placement of the leaves, their shape, the configuration of their margins and the vein pattern will establish the genus and very often the species of the specimen.

The diagrammatical sketches below show leaf placement, shape etc., and give the proper botanical terms which are used throughout the text. The non-specialist may find this section useful for reference.

## VEIN PATTERNS OF LEAVES

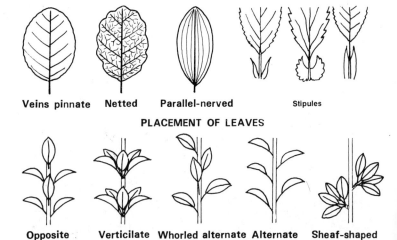

**Veins pinnate**    **Netted**    **Parallel-nerved**    Stipules

## PLACEMENT OF LEAVES

**Opposite**    **Verticilate**    **Whorled alternate**    **Alternate**    **Sheaf-shaped**

## LEAF SHAPES

Kidney-shaped    Orbicular    Ovate    Obovate    Cunate

Spathulate   Rhomboid   Triangulare    Obcordate   Cordate   Arrow-shaped

Lanceolate   Elliptic   Oblong   Linear   Needle-shaped   Pinnately lobed    Pinnate   Bipinnate

Palmately lobed    Digitate    Palmate    Trifoliate

## LEAF MARGINS

Entire    Serrate    Biserrate    Undulate    Crenate    Dentate   Spiny -margined

# KEY TO DEFINITION BY SHAPE OF LEAVES

**Type**                                          **See species number**

needle-shaped, longer than 5 cm, narrower than 1.5 mm: 1, 2, 3, 4, 5, 6, 7, 8

needle-shaped, broad, shorter than 5 cm, wider than 1.5 mm: 9, 10, 11, 21

needle-shaped, shorter than 5 cm, of rather squarish cut: 12

needle-shaped, hard and pointed, placed in whorls of 3: 14, 15, 16, 17

small, scale-shaped, overlapping: 13, 18, 19, 20, 198, 199, 200

linear: 159, 163, 184

very small, linear, in whorls of 3-4: 170

oblong: 85, 146, 169

oblong to lanceolate: 83, 166, 167, 168

oblong to elliptical: 68, 113, 190, 193

elliptical, margins dentate or serrated: 36, 37, 38, 39

elliptical, margins whole: 23, 112, 114, 118, 119, 175

elliptical to lanceolate, with margins dentate, serrated or whole: 110, 124, 125, 126, 161

lanceolate to linear: 44, 78, 155, 156, 160, 162

lanceolate, margins whole: 30, 86, 173, 183, 186

lanceolate, margins dentate or serrated: 43, 109, 177

lanceolate to oval, margins whole or almost whole: 42, 84, 174, 176

lanceolate to oval, margins dentate or serrated: 117, 178

oval and simple, margins serrated or dentate: 27, 41, 66, 111

oval to triangular: 120, 154

oval to oblong: 29, 40, 157, 172

oval to disc-shaped: 28, 68, 153

20

| **Type** | **See species number** |

oval to elliptical, margins whole, serrated or dentate: 107, 115, 130, 140, 141, 142, 143, 144, 145, 150, 165, 171, 194, 195

obovate and simple, margins serrated or dentate: 22, 34, 35, 123

obovate to oblong: 164, 192

obovate to sphenoid: 158, 185

obovate to elliptical: 105, 108, 116

disc-shaped: 79

disc- to heart-shaped: 87, 88, 89, 121, 122

oval to lanceolate, or obovate to lanceolate, with asymmetrical base, margins serrated: 127, 128, 129

oval to lanceolate, with very pointed tip: 131, 132, 189

oval or shallowly 3-lobed: 97, 99

palmately lobed or dentate: 152

palmately lobed, whorled, alternate, without stipules: 24, 25, 26

palmately lobed, alternate, with base cordate, without stipules: 70, 32

palmately lobed, big, with stipules attached to the petiole: 69

palmately lobed or pinnately lobed, shorter than 5 cm. Whorled, alternate, with cunate base and with stipules: 45, 46, 47, 48, 49, 50, 51

palmately lobed, opposite: 90, 91, 92, 93, 94, 95, 96, 98, 191

palmate: 100, 182

palmate, larger than 50 cm, with more than 15 linear leaflets: 197

pinnately lobed or dentate: 139

pinnately lobed: 133, 134, 135, 136, 137, 138

pinnate, opposite, without stipules: 179, 180, 181, 187, 188

pinnate, whorled, alternate, without stipules: 31, 33, 71, 80, 81, 101, 102, 103, 104, 106, 151

pinnate, larger than 1 cm, with more than 20 leaflets: 196

pinnate, whorled, alternate with 5-9 leaflets and stipules at the base of petiole: 57, 58, 59, 60, 61, 62, 63, 64, 65

trifoliate or pinnate with 5 leaflets, whorled alternate, with stipules attached to petiole: 52, 53, 54, 55, 56

trifoliate, whorled, alternate without stipules: 72, 73, 74, 75, 76, 77

trifoliate with stipules not attached to petiole: 82

*Tree of Heaven (Ailanthus altissimus) was first introduced into Greece from China in the 19th century and has since become self-propagating, as have certain other foreign species.*

# THE PARTS OF FLOWERS AND FRUITS

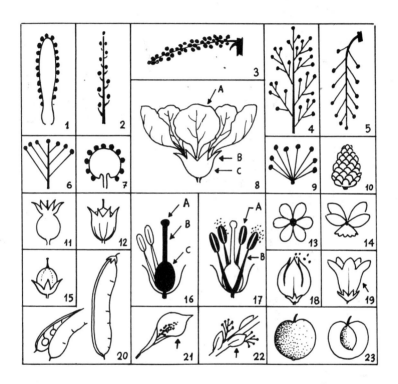

## Key to Illustrations

1. spadix   2. spike   3. catkin   4. compound raceme   5. raceme
6. corymb   7. capitulum   8a. petal   8b. sepal   8c. calyx   9. sheaf
10. cone   11. ovary inferior   12. ovary innate   13. flower radial
14. flower zygomorphic   15. ovary superior   16a. stigma   16b. style
16c. ovary   17. stamen   17a. anther   17b. filament   18. capsule
19. corolla   20. legume   21. spathe   22. bract   23. drupe

*A forest of CEPHALONIAN FIR on Mr Oiti in Central Greece.*

# THE GENERA

Greece has about 200 species of tree and large shrub which belong to 70 different genera. To assist the non-specialist, the main characteristics of each genus are given below, before the main text with the individual description of the various species.

### Pine (genus *Pinus*)

Large evergreen trees, with rounded or pyramidal crowns. Leaves linear, growing 2-5 from a common papery bract. Seedlings with leaves singular. Flowers small, conical, males in clusters at branch terminals of last year's wood; females grouped 1-5 in rounded, properly conical, or more rarely cylindrical cones. Seeds hard, attached to membraneous wings, growing in twos protected by the individual woody scales of the cone.

### Fir (genus *Abies*)

Large evergreen trees with pyramidal crowns and whorled branches. Leaves single, linear, resinous, growing spirally along the branch or in two flat ranks, comb-fashion. Small cone-shaped male flowers in the leaf axils on last year's wood. Female flowers in cylindrical cones always upright, on branches near the top of the tree. Mature cone scales woody and not very thick. Seeds 2 per scale, rather hard and enveloped in a papery membrane when ripe. On maturity, cone scales flake off and drop.

### Spruce (genus *Picea*)

Large evergreen trees with usually straight trunks and whorled branches. Leaves linear, usually square, growing irregularly spaced densely all round and along the branch. If the base of each needle has a little "peg" which tears away when the needle is pulled, this identifies the tree as a spruce. Flowers small, cone shaped. Males growing in clusters, females in long cylindrical cones at the branch terminals, drooping as they mature. Cone scales do not drop off after ripening as in firs. Seeds in twos in membraneous covering.

### Cypress (genus *Cupressus*)

Tall evergreen trees, occasionally growing as shrubs. Branches almost square with short flat leaves overlapping like fish scales, or narrowly linear and opposite. Male flower cones very small, at branch terminals.

Female flower cones small, globular, with 6-14 woody, square-topped scales over many winged seeds.

### Juniper (genus *Juniperus*)

Small evergreen trees or shrubs. Flowers of either sex on separate trees or both on same plant. Leaves linear or scale-shaped, opposite or in groups of three. Very small male flowers in ovate or spherical cones. Female cones rather fleshy, containing hard seeds without membranes.

### Yew (genus *Taxus*)

Evergreen non-resinous trees or shrubs. Leaves flattened linear, spirally arranged, dark green at the top of the tree, lighter green below. Trees either male or female. Male flowers are clusters of yellow stamens in the leaf axils, shedding pollen abundantly; female flowers are green, bud-like, maturing into distinctive red fleshy cups containing 1 hard seed each.

### Berbery (genus *Berberis*)

Evergreen or deciduous shrubs, spiny, with bright yellow wood. Often growing in clumps or hedges. Leaves obovate, spiny-toothed or dentate, with sharp prickles at the base of the leaf stalk. Flowers yellow or orange, with petals which drop off easily; stamens 6. Fruit is a small fleshy drupe containing 1-3 seeds.

### Laurel (genus *Laurus*)

Large evergreen shrubs, also growing as trees, one-sexed or bisexual. Leaves lanceolate, hard and shiny, very aromatic when crushed. Flowers small, 4-petalled, in rounded clusters in the leaf axils. Male and twinsexed flowers have many stamens, female flowers only 4. Fruit is a fleshy drupe.

### Apple (genus *Malus*)

Usually small, deciduous trees with rounded trunks. Leaves simple, pointed or oval, margins serrated, usually growing in bunches from very short woody stalks. Flowers white, 5-petalled, flushed pink on the outside; numerous yellow stamens. Calyx 5-lobed, ovary inferior with 5 styles. The fruit, the apple, in varying sizes and shapes, with 5 seed valves in the centre, separated by tough-skinned membranes, each cell containing 1-2 seeds.

**Pear** (genus *Pyrus*)

Small deciduous trees, rather spiny in the self-propagated form. Leaves simple, whole or lightly dentate. Flowers white, 5-petalled, calyx 5-lobed. Ovary inferior, with 5 styles. Numerous stamens with carmine anthers. The pear fruit varies in shape and size. Core is divided by membranes into 5 chambers, each containing 1-2 seeds.

**Medlar** *(genus Mespilus)*

Small trees with simple, lanceolate to oblong leaves. Flowers white or pink, singly, on twigs surrounded by leaves, 5-petalled. Calyx with 5 triangular and persistent sepals, ovary inferior with 5 styles. Fruit resembles a small brown apple with a broad navel. Seeds rounded and hard.

**Service tree** (genus *Sorbus*)

Deciduous trees or shrubs, with alternate leaves, either simple or compound. Flowers in compound umbels in leaf axils; 5 petals, white or pink, calyx 5-lobed, ovary inferior or superior with 2-5 styles, numerous stamens. Fruit round or pear-shaped, fleshy, red or brown, containing 2-5 seeds.

**Plum** (genus *Prunus* subgenus *Prunus*)

Deciduous trees or shrubs, branches usually spiny at the tips, at least when self-propagated. White 5-petalled flowers appear before the leaves, either singly, in pairs, or in clusters on a common stalk. Calyx 5-lobed, stamens numerous, ovary superior with 1 style. Fruits on short petioles are small, fleshy drupes, containing one oval stony nut.

**Wild cherry** (genus *Prunus* subgenus *Cerasus*)

Usually grows as a deciduous suckering shrub, sometimes as a tree. Leaves varying from oval to elliptical or oblong; small stipules which soon drop. Long-stalked white flowers in clusters, 5-petalled, stamens numerous. Calyx 5-lobed, ovary superior. The fruit is a fleshy drupe hanging on a long stalk, containing a single large hard seed.

**Almond** and **Peach** (genus *Prunus* subgenus *Amygdalus*)

Small deciduous trees. Leaves elliptical to oblong. Flowers white or pink growing singly or in pairs on very short stalks, 5-petalled, many stamens. Calyx 5-lobed, ovary superior. Fruit is an oblong drupe coated in hard inedible flesh which splits to the stone on maturity.

### Hawthorn (genus *Crataegus*)

Deciduous shrubs or small trees, usually spiny. Leaves alternate, simple or pinnately lobed, dentate or serrated, with permanent leaf-like stipules. Flowers pink or white, growing in clusters or, very rarely, singly. Rounded petals 5, calyx 5-lobed, ovary inferior with 1-5 styles. Fruit is a small mealy drupe, usually red, containing 1-5 seeds.

### Wildberries (genus *Rubus*)

Low shrubby plants with many branches either upright or creeping, varying from very thorny to smooth. Alternate leaves either simple or palmately or pinnately compound, with dentate or serrated leaflets, and stipules joined to the base of the petiole. Flowers white, pink or reddish, growing singly or in clusters, 5-petalled; calyx disk-shaped with 5 spreading lanceolate sepals, stamens numerous. Superior ovary with many carpels ripening into small fleshy drupes fused into a berry, which is juicy and usually edible.

### Gooseberry and Currants (genus *Ribes*)

Deciduous shrubs, rarely evergeen, often prickly. Petioled leaves palmately 3-5 lobed; no stipules. Flowers single or in clusters in leaf axils, yellow or pinkish, with 5 sepals, 5 very small petals, 5 stamens. Ovary inferior with 2 styles. Usually edible fruit, a fleshy and juicy berry, green, yellow or red, containing many seeds.

### Wild rose (genus *Rosa*)

Deciduous or evergreen shrubs varying in size, either upright, climbing or rambling, and usually thorny. Leaves pinnately compound, with stipules more or less attached to the base of the stem. Flowers with 5 white, pink, red or yellow petals, calyx with 5 sepals, stamens numerous. Ovary fused, with flask-shaped calyx. Fruit usually red, mealy to fleshy, containing many one-seeded carpels on its inner wall.

### Amelanchier (genus *Amelanchier*)

Deciduous shrubs or small trees. Alternate leaves simple, dentate or serrated, with stipules joined to the petiole base. Small flowers with 5 white petals, calyx with 5 pointed lobes. Stamens numerous. Superior ovary half encircled by the calyx. Fleshy purplish or bluish fruit.

**Pyracantha - Cotoneaster** (genus *Pyracantha and Cotoneaster*)

Deciduous or evergreen shrubs or small trees. Alternate leaves simple, on short stems, margins whole or slightly dentate, with stipules which soon fall. Flowers white or pink, 5-petalled, growing singly or in clusters, stamens numerous. Calyx with 5 small lobes, ovary either inferior or superior. Fruit globular, small and somewhat fleshy, usually red, containing 2-5 seeds.

**Plane** (genus *Platanus* and genus *Liquidambar*)

Large trees, deciduous or almost evergreen. Alternate leaves palmate, with stipules wrapped around the base of the petiole. Flowers small, with 3-8 petals and sepals. The male flowers, resembling catkins, have 3-8 stamens; the female flowers, clustered in dense round heads, have 3-8 pistils.

**Liquidambar** is very similar to Plane, but its leaves lack stipules, and the flowers have no petals.

**Carob** (genus *Ceratonia*)

Evergreen trees with pinnately compound leaves which lack a terminal foliole. Margins whole. Small flowers, yellowish-green or reddish-green, without petals, calyx 5-lobed. Trees usually either male or female, sometimes bisexual. The male flower has 5 long stamens, those on the female flower are short and infertile. The ovary has 2 lobed stigmata. Fruit is a large pod containing many hard seeds.

**Bean trefoil** (genus *Anagyris),* **Laburnum** (g. *Laburnum*), all the **Brooms** in this book (of genera *Calycotome, Lembetropis, Cytisus, Spartium*), **Judas tree** (g. *Cercis*), **Bladder senna** (g. *Colutea*) and **Tree medick** (g. *Medicago*) all belong to the *Leguminosae* or Pea family. They are all deciduous and of shrubby growth with generally straight erect branches, but **Bean trefoil, Laburnum** and **Tree medick** also grow as trees. The leaves are trifoliate, except for genus *Spartium* (simple, narrowly lanceolate), *Colutea* (pinnate), and *Cercis* (disk-shaped). The inflorescence appears generally in the leaf axils, but at the branch terminals for genus *Lembotropis*.

The Pea family takes its name from the resemblance of both its flowers and seeds with those of the familiar pea. The five petals of the flowers are fitted together in such a way as to ensure that every visiting bee is dusted with pollen. Two petals at the base make a "keel", two at the sides are called "wings", and an upright one at the top is the "standard". Within the keel, which the insect must enter to collect nectar, are 5 stamens and a pistil rising from the ovary. After pollination the ovary ripens into a pod containing a number of seeds, which splits open when it is fully ripe and dry. The flowers are usually some shade of yellow, but roseate purple for genus *Cercis.*

## Pomegranate (genus *Punica*)

Deciduous shrubs or small trees. Leaves opposite, oblong, growing in clusters from a common very short woody petiole. Flower red, with 5-7 petals above fleshy 5-7 lobed calyx, also red and bell-shaped. Stamens numerous and long. Inferior ovary is embedded in the calyx. Large fruit, with leathery rind enclosing very many small seeds each in an edible fleshy casing.

## Myrtle (genus *Myrtus*)

Small evergreen trees or shrubs. Leaves opposite, whole, usually aromatic. Flowers 5-petalled, white, with 5-lobed calyx and numerous stamens. Inferior ovary with 2-3 fused carpels. Fruit is small and fleshy

with many seeds.

## Oleaster (genus *Eleagnus*)

Deciduous or evergreen trees. Leaves alternate, whole, silvery and with short petioles. Flowers single or multiple in leaf axils, without petals. Four-lobed calyx tubular or bell-shaped. Stamens 4. Fruit is mealy with 1 hard seed.

## Cistus (genus *Cistus*)

Usually evergreen shrubs of varying size. Opposite leaves oval or lanceolate. Flowers large, 5-petalled, white, pink or purple; 3-5 sepals, stamens numerous. Ovary superior, 5-10 carpels. Fruit is a capsule with as many valves as carpels and persistent calyx.

## Lime (genus *Tilia*)

Large deciduous trees. Alternate leaves with petioles, obliquely heartshaped, pointed. Flower small, limegreen, usually scented, depending in clusters from a long stem which is the extension of a membraneous bract. Petals and sepals 5, stamens numerous and protruding. Ovary superior with 5 cells. Fruit is a hard capsule with 1-3 seeds.

### Maple (genus *Acer*)

Deciduous or occasionally evergreen tree of varying size. Opposite leaves palmately lobed or palmate. Flowers very small, greenish yellow; male and female flowers usually on separate trees, rarely both together. Sepals and petals 5, occasionally 4. Stamens 4-10, generally 8. Ovary superior, 2-celled, ripening into two hardish spheres lightly attached, each with its own membraneous seedwing.

### Horse chestnut (genus *Aesculus*)

Trees or large shrubs, usually deciduous. Opposite leaves palmate on long petioles. Flowers 4-5 petalled, massed in conspicuous spikes, white, yellow or red. Calyx bell-shaped with 4-5 lobes, stamens 5-9. Ovary superior, 3-celled. Fruit a large, thick-skinned capsule with 3 valves containing one large shiny reddish-brown seed each.

### Sweet chestnut (genus *Castanea*)

Deciduous trees or large shrubs. Alternate leaves elliptical or lanceolate. Flowers either male or female. The males in erect catkins, without petals, 6 sepals, 10-20 stamens; female flowers usually in threes inside a prickly covering, with 6 small sepals and inferior ovary. Fruit a thorny capsule, with 1-7 large seeds, the edible chestnuts.

### Terebinth (genus *Pistacia*)

Evergreen or deciduous trees or shrubs with strong resinous scent. Alternate leaves pinnately compound. Small flowers, one-sexed on different plants, no petals. Male flower with 5-lobed calyx and 5 stamens, female flower with 3-4 lobed calyx, simple ovary with 3 stigmata. Fruit a small drupe, more or less fleshy, with single seed.

### Cotinus (genus *Rhus*)

Evergreen or deciduous shrubs, aromatic, with resinous sap. Alternate leaves simple, trifoliate or pinnate. Small flowers bisexual or one-sexed on individual plants, greenish, growing in clusters in leaf axils or terminally. Petals, stamens and calyx-lobes 5. Ovary superior. Fruit a small hard drupe with one seed.

31

**Holly** (genus *Ilex*)

Evergreen or deciduous trees. Alternate leaves on petioles, margin usually spiny-toothed. Flowers white, usually in clusters in the leaf axils, one-sexed for each plant. Calyx 4-lobed, corolla with 4 or rarely 5 petals fused at the base. Stamens 4-5. Ovary superior, with 3-4 cells. The fruit is a red, black or yellow drupe with 2-8 hard seeds.

**Spindle tree** (genus *Euonymous*)

Small upright trees or woody climbers, evergreen or deciduous. Branches more or less square. Leaves opposite, pointed ovals or oblongs, with petioles. Flowers small, whitish, in opposite clusters depending from leaf axils. Calyx 4-5 lobed, 5 petals, 4-5 stamens. Superior ovary with 2-5 cells. Fruit a capsule, seed or berry, with 4-5 rather fleshy lobes containing 1-2 seeds each.

**Buckthorn** (genus *Rhamnus*)

Small deciduous or evergreen trees or shrubs. Alternate leaves opposite, whole or serrated, with small stipules at the petiole base. Flowers in bunches or clusters in the leaf axils, rarely bisexual, usually either male or female on separate trees or on the same tree. Calyx bell-shaped, 4-5 lobed. Petals 4-5, or often non-existant. Stamens 4-5. Ovary superior with 2-4 cells. The fruit is a spherical drupe with 2-4 seeds.

**Cornel tree** (genus *Cornus*)

Generally deciduous trees or shrubs. Leaves opposite, occasionally alternate or whorled. Small flowers growing in umbel-like clusters in leaf axils or at branch terminals. Petals 4, white or yellow, small calyx with 4 small points. Ovary inferior, 2-celled. Fruit is a fleshy drupe with 1 hard seed.

**Birch** (genus *Betula*)

Trees of varying sizes. Alternate leaves simple, with dentate, serrated or wavy margins. Flowers yellowish, in either male or female catkins. Male catkins with 1-3 three-lobed scales, each of which covers 3 flowers without petals or calyx, but having one concave scale and 4 stamens. Female catkins with many 3-lobed scales, each covering 3 flowers with superior ovary. Very small fruit encased in membraneous seedwing.

### Filberts (genus *Corylus*)

Deciduous shrubs or small trees with alternate leaves. Flowers of separate sexes, the male clustered in hanging yellow catkins, without petals, having 1 usually 3-lobed scale and 4 stamens; the female singly or in twos and threes, with 2-celled ovary and 2 carmine styles. Fruit inside a hard woody case contained in a leafy membraneous cup, which is sometimes open at the top and sometimes closed, the serrated membrane forming a toothed apex.

### Alder (genus *Alnus*)

Usually deciduous trees or shrubs with alternate leaves. Flowers in short catkins either male or female, both growing on the same plant. Male flowers small, with 1 scale and 4 stamens, usually growing in threes beneath 5-lobed scales. Female flowers without petals or sepals, consisting only of the ovary which is protected by hard scales layered as in a catkin which, when ripe, resembles a small oval cone.

### Hornbeam (genus *Carpinus*)

Deciduous trees, with alternate leaves on petioles. Flowers in separate male or female catkins on the same tree together. Catkins consist of many layers of quite large leafy membraneous bracts covering the stamens or ovaries respectively. There are neither petals nor sepals. The fruit which develops from the ovaries continues to be protected by the leafy bracts.

### European hop hornbeam (genus *Ostrya*)

Very similar to Hornbeam, genus *Carpinus (q. v.)* above, but each nut enclosed in a conspicuous sac-like bract. Trees have rough bark.

### Elm (genus *Ulmus*)

Deciduous trees, rarely evergreen or nearly so. Alternate leaves, asymmetrical, with stipules which soon fall. Flowers small, usually reddish, with short or long stem, borne in compact clusters; no petals, calyx 4-8 lobed, stamens 4-8, superior ovary with 2 styles. Fruit small, in hard casing at centre of papery seedwing membrane.

### Abelicea (genus *Abelicea* or *Zelkova*)

Evergreen or deciduous trees resembling Elm (genus *Ulmus*), also with alternate leaves. Flowers without petals, calyx 4-5 lobed. Male flowers appear as greenish stamen clusters, females as single bud-structures with 2 pistils. The fruit is small and hard, with projections.

**Nettle tree** (genus *Celtis*)

Trees or large shrubs, deciduous or evergreen. Leaves alternate. Flowers long-stemmed, yellowish-green, bisexual or male and female separately; no petals, calyx 5-lobed. Male flowers in bunches, female and bisexual flowers singly. Fruit is a drupe containing one seed.

**Oak** (genus *Quercus*)

Deciduous or evergreen trees attaining considerable size. Alternate leaves simple or lobed, with small stipules which soon fall. Male flower with 4-8 sepals and 4-12 stamens, growing in hanging catkin clusters. Female flowers singly or several together, with 5-10 very small sepals, and ovary with 3-4 styles. Fruit surrounded by scaly or spiny cup encircling lower part of acorn, which itself varies from almost round to long oval.

**Beech** (genus *Fagus*)

Deciduous trees, with alternate elliptical leaves. Male flowers in greenish spherical catkins, females growing singly or in pairs. Triangular beechnut fruit resembling a small chestnut in its woody, spiny case.

**Christ-thorn** (genus *Paliurus*)

Deciduous or almost evergreen spiny trees or shrubs. Alternate leaves, obliquely oval with 3 veins. Flowers small, greenish-yellow, with 5 sepals, 5 two-lobed petals, 5 stamens. Fruit small, hard and hemispherical, enclosed in a circular membraneous seedwing.

**Walnut** (genus *Juglans*)

Deciduous trees. Alternate leaves pinnately compound, aromatic. One-sexed flowers both on the same plant. Male flowers without petals, their calyx 2-5 lobed with 6-30 stamens, growing in hanging catkins. Female flowers flask-shaped, upright, with 4-lobed calyx and inferior ovary; several of them together in the leaf axils. Fruit a large drupe with dense fleshy outside covering over large seed encased in woody shell when fully mature.

**Poplar** (genus *Populus*)

Deciduous trees, leaves alternate with long petioles. Flowers in hanging catkins, male and female on separate trees. Male flower is a small cup-shaped bract with 8-20 stamens; female flower, one simple ovary covered by dentate or jagged bracts. Bracts in both sexes are usually pubescent. The elongated seeds, also tufted with hair, split into four.

### Willow (genus *Salix*)

Deciduous trees or shrubs. Leaves alternate, occasionally almost opposite, with stipules which either fall early or remain on the branch permanently. Flowers massed in elongated or short hairy upright catkins, male and female on separate trees. The catkins consist of small scales beneath which grow 2-5 stamens (male flower), or the ovary (female flower).

### Box (genus *Buxus*)

Evergreen shrub with small leaves, opposite and glossy. Flowers one-sexed, both types on the same plant. Female flower with superior ovary and 6 sepals; male flower with 4 sepals and 4 stamens, in clusters around the female flowers. Fruit, an obovate or spherical capsule with 3 black seeds in separate valves.

### Rhododendron (genus *Rhododendron*)

Evergreen or deciduous shrubs or small trees. Alternate simple leaves, whole margins, glossy surface. Large flowers in bunches, usually at branch terminals. Corolla with tubular base and usually 5 twisted petals. Calyx 5-lobed, stamens 5-10 or more. Fruit is a round capsule containing many seeds.

### Arbutus (genus *Arbutus*)

Evergreen trees or small shrubs. Alternate leaves whole or dentate. Flower white or pink, corolla flask-shaped or round, with 5 serrations at the mouth. Calyx small, also with 5 serrations. Stemmed flowers borne in dependent clusters. Fruit is a fleshy drupe with many seeds.

### Heather (genus *Erica*)

Evergreen shrubs with erect branches. Leaves dense, very small, linear, growing in threes and fives. Flower white, pink, greenish or brownish. Corolla bell- or flask-shaped, 4-lobed at the mouth. Calyx 4-lobed, 8 stamens. Fruit a small capsule, with 4 cells and many seeds.

**Date Plum** (genus *Diospyrus*)

Deciduous or evergreen trees or shrubs. Alternate leaves, rarely opposite, with whole margins. Flowers bisexual or one-sexed for each tree, clustered in the leaf axils, or single if female only. Calyx with 4-7 lobes. Corolla creamy-white, with 4-7 lobes and 8-16 stamens. Ovary superior, with 2-6 styles. Fruit inedible, juicy, spherical, with 1-10 broad seeds.

**Storax** (genus *Styrax*)

Deciduous or evergreen shrubs or small trees. Alternate leaves with whole margins. Flowers white, usually in hanging sprays. Calyx bell-shaped, with 5-7 petals joined at the base, 10-16 stamens. Fruit is a leathery drupe with 1-2 seeds.

**Oleander** (genus *Nerium*)

Evergreen shrub, with lanceolate leaves usually growing in threes. Flowers white, pink or yellowish, with 5 petals joined at the base in a cylindrical corollary tube. Calyx 5-lobed, stamens 5. Fruit a long narrow pod, twisting as it splits into two lengthwise when mature. Numerous small seeds tufted with hair.

**Olive** (genus *Olea*)

Evergreen trees or shrubs, occasionally spiny. Leaves opposite or in threes, margins whole. Flowers small, cruciform, white or creamy, clustered in leaf axils. Calyx small, usually 4-lobed, stamens 2, ovary superior. The fruit is a fleshy drupe with 1 oval seed more or less elongated.

**Privet** (genus *Ligustrum*)

Deciduous or evergreen shrubs with opposite leaves. Flowers small, white, corolla 4-lobed at the mouth of corolla tube; small bell-shaped calyx; 2 stamens. Fruit is a drupe, usually black, fleshy, with 1-4 seeds.

**Mock Privet** (genus *Phillyrea*)

Evergreen shrub or small tree. Leaves opposite, simple. Flowers small, greenish or yellowish, with cruciform corolla and small calyx. Fruit is a fleshy black drupe.

**Lilac** (genus *Syringa*)

Evergreen or deciduous shrubs. Opposite leaves simple, very rarely pinnate, margins whole. Flowers in pyramidal clusters at branch terminals. Calyx 4-lobed. Corolla cruciform, stamens 2, ovary with 2 cells. Fruit an oblong or oval capsule containing 2 seeds.

**Ash** (genus *Fraxinus*)

Deciduous trees, with opposite leaves, pinnately compound. Flowers small, in hanging clusters, either with 4 petals or none, calyx 4-lobed. Fruit a small hard seed, with a long narrow membraneous seedwing.

**Chaste tree** (genus *Vitex*)

Evergreen or deciduous tree or shrub. Opposite leaves, palmately compound, rarely simple. Flowers brownish pink in spiked upright clusters, with corolla tube ending in 5 lobes, each almost two-lipped. Stamens 4, calyx 5-lobed, ovary superior. Fruit a drupe, with one seed segmented into 4 parts.

**Tea-tree** (genus *Lycium*)

Evergreen or deciduous small trees or shrubs, usually spiny. Leaves alternate or in clusters, simple, margins whole. Flowers brownish, purple or white, singly or clustered in leaf axils. Corolla tube spreading into 5 lobes. Calyx small, two- or five-lipped. Stamens generally 5. Fruit a fleshy round drupe, red, black or yellow.

**Elder** (genus *Sambucus*)

Usually deciduous shrubs or small trees. Leaves pinnately compound. Flowers numerous, in large dense clusters, small, cream-coloured. Corolla radially symmetrical on very short tube, 5-lobed. Stamens 5. Fruit a fleshy drupe.

**Viburnum** (genus *Viburnum*)

Evergreen or deciduous shrub. Opposite leaves simple or palmately lobed. Flowers small, usually white, with 5-lobed corolla, and calyx with 5 small indentations. Stamens 5, ovary simple. Fruit a fleshy drupe with 1 seed.

## Honeysuckle (genus *Lonicera*)

Deciduous or occasionally evergreen shrubs, climbing, creeping or upright. Opposite leaves with whole margins, no petiole, and often opposite pairs joined at the base one to other. Flowers white, pink flushed, creamy-yellow or deep pink, with corolla tube two-lipped at the mouth. Calyx small with 5 indentations, ovary inferior. Inflorescence in clusters on a common stalk at branch terminals or in leaf axils. Fruit round fleshy drupes clustered together, yellow, bright red, purplish or black.

## Palm (genus *Phoenix*)

Trees of varying height, no branches. Leaves springing directly from the trunk, close together near the top of the bole. Leaves very large, compoundly pinnate with narrow, linear folioles. Flowers small, with 6-lobed corolla, the males with 6 stamens, the females with superior ovary. Inflorescence in large, long-stalked bunches, breaking from tough membraneous sheath. Fruit either a fleshy drupe, or hard-shelled capsule.

## Dwarf fan palm (genus *Chamaerops*)

Dwarf palm with short thick trunk. Leaves large, palmately compound, very many fringelike folioles. Flowers in dense hanging bunches, males with 6-9 stamens. Fruit a hard, inedible drupe.

## Tamarisk (genus *Tamarix*)

Small trees or shrubs with tiny, alternate needle-like or scale-like leaves. Numerous very small flowers in dense elongated clusters. Sepals and petals 4 or 5, stamens the same or twice that number. Ovary one-celled, styles 3-5. The fruit a capsule containing seeds with long silky hairs.

*Young ALEPPO PINES, with a few mature specimens among them, establishing themselves in the scrubland of the* **maquis.** *In the foreground, a clump of STRAWBERRY TREES.*

# THE SPECIES

## Pines

### 1. Aleppo pine *(Pinus halepensis* Miller*)*

This is a very common pine in southern Greece and the islands, where it is found at heights up to 1,000 m at the most. It is one of the dry-leaved, heat-loving species which will flourish in arid and limey soils, or in places where the summer is long and parched. The crown of young trees is pyramidal, but in maturity it takes on an irregular shape, and the trunk develops spiral fluting. The cones, which hang downwards and take two years to ripen, are oval with a rounded tip. It is from the trunk of this tree that the resin is taken which is used in the manufacture of the traditional Greek retsina wine. (For description of genus see p. 25)

### 2. Calabrian pine *(Pinus brutia* Ten.*)*

This is similar to the Aleppo pine above, but grows taller and more vigorously and with a straighter, thicker trunk and longer needles. It is found in the islands of the southern and eastern Aegean, in Thrace, Halkidiki, and in certain parts of Crete. (For description of genus see p. 25)

### 3. Umbrella pine *(Pinus pinea* L.*)*

This, the pine tree of the ancient Greeks, has large cones which provide the edible white pine-kernels used in mediterranean cookery. It takes on its characteristic umbrella shape, which distinguishes it from all other Greek pines, quite early on in its development. Umbrella pine prefers to grow in sand or sandy soils at low altitudes, and is often found near the sea, in such areas as the eastern mainland, the Peloponnese, the Aegean islands and Halkidiki. (For description of genus see p. 25)

**1, 2, 3** *Aleppo pine*      **4** *Calabrian pine*      **5, 6** *Umbrella pine*

41

#### 4. Black pine *(Pinus nigra* Arn.*)*

This is a species found in the highland zones. Its perfectly straight trunk supports very regular whorls of branches set at clearly defined intervals up the bole. Black pine is found at altitudes of 500-1,900 m over a wide geographical area. In the mountains of Crete it replaces the fir, in the Peloponnese it is found mixed in with the Cephalonian fir, on the mainland it has almost disappeared, and in the Agrapha mountain range in the north it forms mixed clumps with other forest trees. Extensive stands of this species exist on the Pindus mountains and in the mountains of West and Central Macedonia. The needles of Black pine are of medium size; the small cones mature in one year. A hardy species even in the most unfavourable conditions of soil and climate, it has been used with complete success during the past twenty years in reafforesting the most barren and eroded stretches on high ground. (For description of genus see p. 25)

#### 5. Scots pine *(Pinus silvestris* L.*)*

This tree of the highland belt is similar to the Black pine above. Its equally straight trunk develops a pinkish-grey bark with deep vertical fissures in maturity. The younger and higher branches are often a striking orange red. Young trees have a pyramidal crown, but the trunk of older trees rises up bare of branches until there is a broad tassel of foliage at the very top. This species is the tallest of the Greek pines, with a mature height of 40 m. Its needles are relatively small, up to 9 cm long, and bluish green. The cones are also small, sharply pointed ovals, and take 2 years to mature. Scots pine is found on some Macedonian and Thracian mountains, and in certain parts of the Pindus range. (For description of genus see p. 25)

**1, 2, 3** *Black pine*     **4, 5** *Scots pine*

## 6. Balkan pine *(Pinus heldreichii* Christ.)

This evergreen conifer grows happily at altitudes of 1,500-2,400 m where no other Greek tree will survive. The trunk is straight and densely covered with branches. The needles, in characteristic tufts at the ends of the twigs, are hard and set very close together to counteract moisture loss. The cones are small and ripen next spring. The most characteristic feature of this tree is the great number of fissures up the trunk. Heldreich pine timber, exceptionally strong and resistant to rot, is used in the manufacture of many tools as well as household equipment. (For description of genus see p. 25)

## 7. Mountain pine *(Pinus montana Miller* s. sp. *uncinata)*

This relatively small tree is supported by a slim, straight trunk. Its needles are short, no more than 5 cm, and the stalkless cones also measure only from 2-5 cm in length. Mountain pine grows in Macedonia and Thrace, at altitudes of up to 2,000 m. (For description of genus see p. 25)

## 8. Macedonian pine *(Pinus peuce* Grieseb.)

A distinctive feature of this relatively low tree is that the branches extend horizontally from almost the very base of the trunk, which gives this pine something of the appearance of a bush. This species is very different from the other Greek pines also with regard to its needles, which are not set in pairs but in clusters of five. The cones are considerably longer and more slender than those of other pines, and rather resemble those of the fir. Macedonian pine is rare in Greece, and can be found only in certain border-area mountains of Macedonia and Thrace. (For description of the genus see p. 25)

**1, 2, 3, 4** *Balkan pine*   **5** *Mountain pine*   **6** *Macedonian pine*

# Firs

*In antiquity, the Silver fir was sacred to Artemis, the moon goddess who presided over childbirth, and it long remained the tree symbolizing birth in more modern Europe. Also, it was timber from fir trees which King Solomon expressly chose for the building of his chief temples.*

## 9. Cephalonian or Greek fir *(Abies cephalonica* Loudon)

Mature trees of this species reach a size of up to 30 m. The straight, smooth cylindrical trunk supports a pyramidal crown, with the branches beginning from quite low down on the tree. The needles are hard and spiny, about 22 cm long; at the lower end they are marked by two parallel lighter-coloured lines; they emerge from all round the twig in apparently haphazard order. The long, slim cones (15-20 cm), which are borne upright, grow on the branches near the top of the tree. They develop to full maturity by the end of the autumn, when all the scales flake off completely, leaving only the central spindle standing on the branch. Cephalonian fir is an exclusively Greek tree, flourishing wherever there are extensive mountain forests, from the Agrapha range in the north to the Taygetus range in the Peloponnese. It can be found further north as far as the border areas, but only in small clumps among other trees. The altitude for this species ranges from between 600-2,000 m. (For description of genus see p. 25)

## 10. Silver.fir *(Abies pectinata* Loud. or *A. alba* Miller)

A large tree, not uncommonly up to 40 m in height and occasionally more, Silver fir has a completely straight trunk with the branches extending horizontally and forming a narrow, pyramidal crown. The needles grow comb-fashion in two opposed rows along the length of the shoot, and terminate not in a point but in two blunt lobes. The slim cylindrical cones are typical of the genus, but somewhat smaller, never exceeding 15 cm. Silver fir grows in the mountains of Epirus, Macedonia and Thrace, close to the borders with Greece's Balkan neighbours. (For description of genus see p. 25)

**1, 2, 3** *Cephalonian fir*     **4, 5** *Silver fir*

### 11. **Macedonian fir** *(Abies borisii regis* Mattf.*)*

This fir, to be found in the mountains of northern Greece, is a natural hybrid of the two described above (Cephalonian and Silver fir) and presents the characteristics of both. The needles are sometimes pointed and sometimes twin-lobed at the tip, two-ranked in comb-fashion, or scattered randomly along the length of the twig. The cones are of intermediate size. (For description of genus see p. 25)


## Spruces

*The Bacchante of the ancient Thracian and Thessalian revels, who in their wild frenzy tore animals and men limb from limb, are stated by Robert Graves to have probably been intoxicated on spruce ale, brewed from the sap, and laced with ivy.*


### 12. **Common** or **Norway spruce** *(Picea excelsa* Link *Picea Abies)*

This is the only species of crimson-barked spruce in Europe. It grows to a very large tree, easily reaching heights of 50 m and more. The trunk is very straight, with horizontal branches forming the normal spruce crown which is pyramidal like that of firs, but somewhat fuller just below the tip. The needles resemble those of the fir but are thinner; they drop easily, leaving behind the small peglike projections at their base which give the bare branches their characteristically rough appearance. The female flowers are crimson and upright at first; the drooping cones are long and slim like those of the fir, but smaller. After shedding their seeds they fall from the tree intact, without the platelets having flaked off first. Norway spruce (which provides the Swedish "whitewood" timber, has bark rich in tannin, and is a source of resin as well as pitch) is very widespread in Europe; in Greece it is found only near the Greek-Bulgarian border, in the famous Kara-Dere forest in the Rhodopi mountains. (For description of genus see p. 25)

**1, 2** *Macedonian fir*    **3, 4** *Common spruce*

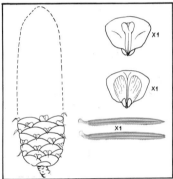

# Cypresses

*At ancient Corinth and Messene, the cypress was sacred to Artemis Cranae, and cypress groves enclosed the goddess' sanctuaries. In the Orphic mysteries the tree symbolises resurrection, and it is still the prime symbol of resurrection in mediterranean churchyards.*

### 13. Italian cypress *(Cupressus sempervirens L.)*

This is a large tree with a straight trunk and pyramidal crown, reaching heights of up to 40 m. It is the only self-propagating species of cypress in Greece, and is to be found particularly in Crete, the Dodecanese, and on some other islands in the Ionian and Aegean seas. The overlapping needle-scales are very small and hard, and almost completey cover the wood of the young twig. The round cones, diameter 2-3 cm, reach maturity two years after flowering. The individual square-topped sections then expand outward and the seeds are released. This species is also used as a decorative tree in parks and, because of its great resistance to drought, for reafforestation in hot, dry areas.

Variants from the form described above are *C. cereiformis,* which has a particularly narrow, tapering crown, and *C. pyramidalis,* with more spreading branches. (For description of genus see p. 25)

# Junipers

### 14. Syrian juniper *(Juniperus drupacea Labill.)*

The straight trunk and pyramidal crown of this tree may measure heights of up to 18 m, though usually much less. Its needles are linear, hard, and sharply pointed, varying in length from 1.5-2.5 cm on the same tree, and can be as broad as 4 mm. They are arranged in whorls of three up the length of the twig. The cone which contains the seeds is round, grey-greeen in colour, and has a diameter of 2.5 cm. This species originates from Central Asia, and is found in Greece only on the slopes of the Parnona range in the Peloponnese and on the Karlik mountain near Rhodopi in Thrace. (For description of genus see p. 26)

**1, 2** *Italian cypress*     **3** *Syrian juniper*

### 15. Berried or Prickly juniper *(Juniperus oxycedrus* L.*)*

The trunk of this small tree of large shrub (up to 7 m) is either straight or somewhat distorted. The needles are again linear, hard and pointed, up to 22 mm in length, and grow in successive whorls of three along the twig. The seed, a globular, somewhat fleshy berry, is spherical, less than 1 cm in diameter, and yellow to purplish brown. This species which prefers barren, stony mountain areas, can be found all over Greece and, together with shrubs and bushes, in the arid stretches of the mediterranean landscape known as the *maquis*. (For description of genus see p. 26)

### 16. Sea juniper *(Juniperus macrocarpa* S. and Sm.*)*

This is a bushy small tree of up to 10 m in height, sometimes with a straight trunk, at other times twisted and distorted. Sea cedar resembles Berried juniper *(q.v.)*, but its fruit is almost twice as large, around 12-15 mm in diameter, and brown to black in colour. As its name implies, the species grows in sandy or stony soils, close to the sea. It is to be found in Attica, on Crete, and the Aegean islands. (For description of genus see p. 26)

### 17. Common juniper *(Juniperus communis* L.*)*

This species is rather more of a shrub, but is also found as a straight-boled small tree of up to 7 m. Occasionally the trunk may divide into several spreading branches, covered in fragrant pinkish grey bark. The needles, which have a sharp resinous scent, are again in whorls of three, hard and pointed, and have a silvery band of wax on their upper surface which restricts water loss. They vary in size from 5-18 mm on the same tree. The small, juicy berry, 6-8 mm in diameter, turns a purplish grey-black in the year after pollination. Each berry is really a modified cone, made up of 8 scales hiding the seeds under the pulp. A species of the highland zone, Common juniper is well known throughout all of mainland Greece.

It is from the distilled fruits of this tree that oil of juniper is obtained, which is used for flavouring gin (a drink called after the French word for juniper - *genevrier*). Juniper wood is very highly flammable, even on the bush.

There are many subspecies of Common juniper, chief among them **Dwarf juniper** *(J. communis* L. var. *nana,* Wild, Loudon), which grows as a spreading shrub at heights above 1,800 m. (For description of genus see p. 26)

**1, 2** *Berried juniper*   **3, 4** *Sea juniper*   **5** *Common juniper*

### 18. Great or Greek juniper *(Juniperus excelsa* Bieb.)*

This juniper has a straight trunk topped by a pyramidal crown, and may reach heights of up to 18 m. Its foliage consists of small triangular scales grouped in twos or threes along the shoots. The drupes are black in colour and 12-18 cm across, each containing 4-6 hard seeds. Great juniper flourishes in dry soils in the mountains of Macedonia, Crete, Karpathos, Syros and Euboea, and in the islands of the northern Aegean. (For description of genus see p. 26)

### 19. Stinking juniper *(Juniperus foetidissima* Willd.)*

This tree attains only medium height, growing no larger than about 12 m, and is densely foliated. The leaves of the young saplings are linear, pointed and hard, while on mature trees they have modified into small pointed scales. The drupes are round, black or dark grey in colour, and contain 1-2 seeds each. This is a tree which flourishes at high altitudes up to 2,000 m, growing in limited stands in the mountains of mainland Greece. (For description of genus see p. 26)

### 20. Phoenician juniper *(Juniperus phoenicea* L.)*

This bushily spreading small tree of up to 8 m in height has a straight trunk with branches extending horizontally right from the base to form a pyramidal crown. The overlapping leaves resemble small ovate scales and completely cover the wood of the branch. The drupes are rusty-red, spherical, 6-9 mm in diameter; they contain 3-9 angular and furrowed seeds each. Phoenician juniper has many subspecies, varying in shape and size of fruit. It grows on the dry limestone slopes of southern Greece and the islands, and up to altitudes of 1,200 m. (For description of genus see p. 26)

**1** *Great juniper*    **2, 3** *Stinking juniper*    **4, 5** *Phoenician juniper*

# Yew

*In the folklore and mythology of Europe, the yew was regarded everywhere as the death tree, and in Greece and Italy it was sacred to Hecate. This reputation may in part stem from the fact that the yew casts so deep a shade that nothing else will grow under it. Yew wood having greater elasticity than any other makes the best bows for archers - as the Romans learned from the Greeks. It is thought possible that the Latin name* taxus *is connected with the Greek word* toxon *for bow, and* toxicon *for the poison with which the arrowheads were smeared.*

## 21. Yew tree *( Taxus baccata L.)*

A slow-growing and surprisingly long-lived tree of 10-15 m in height, the yew has spreading or sometimes slightly drooping branches and thrives on chalky soils. Both trunk and bark are usually deeply fluted and fissured, and rarely properly round. Yew, unlike other conifers, easily grows new shoots when cut down. Its leaves resemble those of the fir, but are softer; they are paler in colour on the underside and fall only after several years of life. Male trees have conspicuously yellow flowers in spring, releasing masses of pollen. The female flower develops into distinctive red fruits, the pulp containing one hard and highly poisonous seed about 1 mm in size. The drupe itself is cup-shaped, with the greenish-black seed protruding at the mouth. Yews are to be found on the highest parts of the mountains of all of mainland Greece, either standing alone or in small clumps; others may be found at lower altitudes in relatively cool regions, mixed in with other forest trees. (For description of genus see p. 26)

# Berberies

## 22. Common berbery *(Berberis vulgaris L.)*

This is a bushy shrub, growing 1-3 m tall, with spiky branches. The leaves are obovate with spiny-toothed margins. The small bell-shaped flower has 6 yellow petals and 6 sepals and grows in short racemes of about a dozen or so from the leaf axils. The berry is fleshy, oval, and a bright red. *B. vulgaris* is found in the forests of northern Greece.

**Cretan berbery** *(B. cretica),* to be found in the mountains of that island, develops into quite a small shrub of about 80 cm, has small narrow leaves, the typical yellow flowers, but black fruit. (For description of genus see p. 26)

**1, 2, 3** *Yew tree*    **4, 5** *Common berbery*

# Laurel

*Laurels have since antiquity been associated with poetic inspiration. The female celebrants of the Triple Goddess at Tempe in northern Greece chewed laurel leaves to induce poetic and erotic frenzy, and when Apollo took over the oracle at Delphi, the Pythian priestess there chewed laurel for oracular inspiration. Later such excesses were frowned upon, and the laurel crown was worn with chaster decorum by victors of contests in the arts (under Apollo's patronage) and sports.*

### 23. Laurel or Sweet bay *(Laurus nobilis* L.)

The limbs of this multi-branched evergreen shrub or small tree of up to 10 m tall tend to be rather straight and pointing straight upwards. The leaves are set alternately, elliptical-lanceolate in shape, with a hard leathery surface for protection against moisture loss, and carried on short petioles. The creamy-yellow flowers grouped in the leaf axils develop into small black drupes resembling small olives. Laurel grows all over Greece on the lower reaches of warm mountain slopes, side by side with other shrubs and small trees. Its preference, however, is for ravines and cooler, damper locations. (For description of genus see p. 26)

# Gooseberry and Currants

### 24. Gooseberry *(Ribes grossularia* L.)

This spiny shrub grows up to 1.5 m tall. Its dense, stiff branches have stout, orange-coloured thorns. The alternate, almost disk-shaped leaves are pubescent on the underside, and have 3-5 dentate lobes on a heart-shaped to sphenoid base. The flowers are small, greenish or greenish-red, growing singly or in pairs in the leaf axils. The pubescent calyx has spreading sepals, and the small petals are borne erect. The fruit is round and fleshy with a multitude of small seeds, greenish or yellowish or reddish in colour, and usually hairy as well as glandular. Gooseberry grows in scrubland and forest areas almost anywhere in Greece. (For description of genus see p. 28)

### 25. Parnassian currant *(Ribes multiflorum* Kit.)

This tough-branched, 1.5 m tall shrub has leaves 6-10 cm broad, pubescent on the underside, disk-shaped on a rather heart-shaped base, and divided into 3-5 dentate lobes. Both flowers and fruit grow in hanging

**1, 2, 3** *Laurel* **4, 5** *Gooseberry*

2

3

4

5

racemes 12-16 cm long. The flower sepals are recurved, and the greenish-yellow petals very small. The globular fruit is fleshy, dark red and glossy. This species grows in the mountains of mainland Greece and the northern Peloponnese. (For description of genus see p. 28)

### 26. Oriental currant *(Ribes orientale Pour.)*

This species has pubescent and rather smaller and thinner branches than the two described above. The leaves are kidney-shaped, with 3-5 dentate lobes. Each plant is either male or female. The flowers always grow in erect racemes; they are yellowish, with a bell-shaped calyx, and the sepals (smaller than the petals) are recurved at the tip. The fruits are round and juicy, light-red and hairy. Oriental currant grows in sub-alpine rocky locations in the mountains of mainland Greece and the Peloponnese. (For description of genus see p. 28)

# Apple

*In Celtic legend the wild apple, or quert, was "the noblest tree of all", being the tree of immortality. King Arthur went to the secret island of apple trees to be healed of his wounds. Golden apples abound in legends and fairytales. Mythological Hercules was called Milon because his worshippers offered him apples (milo in Greek). The apple was sacred to Venus Aphrodite also, whose symbol was the five-pointed star formed by the seeds when an apple is halved horizontally.*

### 27. Wild apple *(Malus communis D.C., M. pumila Mill.)*

This is a small deciduous tree with many branches. Its leaves are ovate with serrated margins, pointed at the tip, shiny above and downy on the underside. The petiole is about half the length of the leaf. The radial flower has five round white petals tinged with pink beneath and around their edges, and many bright yellow stamens. The flowers grow in tight bunches on short stalks, several of them emerging from the same bud. The fruit is much like that of the cultivated apple, but only up to 3 cm in diameter, round, green or red, and very tart, being edible only when it is

**1** *Parnassian currant*　　**2** *Oriental currant*　　**3, 4, 5, 6** *Wild apple*

1

2

3

4

5

6

thoroughly ripe. Wild apple flourishes in the Greek highland forests and pastures. It can be found all over the mainland, but is most at home in northern Greece. (For description of the genus see p. 26)

## Pears

**28. Wild pear** *(Pyrus communis* L. s.sp. *pyraster* Borkh.)*

This is the small deciduous ancestor of the cultivated pear. It has small ovate or round leaves, shallowly dentate, hairy when young and glossy in maturity, borne on long slim petioles. The radial flower has 5 white petals and stamens with deep crimson anthers; a number of flowers emerge bunched together from the same bud. The fruit is similar to that of a small garden pear. It is tart, however, and edible only when it has reached advanced maturity. Wild pear is to be found in the highlands of northern Greece. (For description of genus see p. 27)

**29. Almond pear** *(Pyrus amygdaliformis* Vill.)*

This is a small deciduous tree of usually contorted growth, with alternate long narrow leaves, oblong or ovoid. Its flowers, pure white with crimson anthers, resemble those of Wild pear *(q.v.)*. The fruit is smaller, however, and rather more rounded in outline, somewhat like the outer case of an almond, as the name implies. It is extremely tart and has to be very ripe indeed before it can be eaten at all. Almond pear is to be found in barren soils at medium altitudes all over Greece. (For description of genus see p. 27)

## Medlar

**30. Medlar** *(Mespilus germanica* L.)*

In its wild, self-propagated form medlar grows either as small tree or a large bush with slightly spiny branches. It has large, lanceolate leaves, pubescent on top and glossy on the underside. The radial flower, white or pink with 5 petals, grows singly on very short stalks among clusters of leaves. The fruit has the same outer shape as that of the loquat - resembling a small round plum with a navel - but is brown in colour. It

**1, 2** *Wild pear*     **3, 4, 5** *Almond pear*     **6** *Medlar*

contains large hard stones in a scant covering of flesh and is sour to the taste. It should be eaten when it is so ripe that it might pass for rotten. Medlar grows in the forests of northern Greece, at which latitude it is also cultivated in gardens and orchards. (For description of genus see p. 27)

## Service trees

### 31. Service tree *(Sorbus domestica* L.*)*

This large deciduous tree not infrequently attains heights of 20 m. It has compound leaves, each composed of 10-17 dentate leaflets. The white or pink radial flowers are 8-10 mm across, with 5 petals and hairy calyxes, growing in large compound umbels at the branch terminals. The 2.5 cm fruit resembles a shapeless pear, is variegated red and green, and edible in late autumn when it is overripe. True service tree is a highland species of all of mainland Greece. Elsewhere it is planted as much for its general ornamental qualities as for its fruit. (For description of genus see p. 27)

### 32. Wild service tree *(Sorbus torminalis* (L.) Crantz*)*

This deciduous tree grows up to 15 m tall, its dense foliage forming a neatly spherical crown. The leaves are conspicuously palmately lobed, pointed, and serrated at the margins. The small, white, 5-petalled flowers grow in compound umbels. The little drupes are spotted brown, and edible when ripe. This tree is cultivated as an ornamental plant, because its leaves turn a spectacular red in the autumn. In its self-propagated form it is found in northern Greek forests. (For description of genus see p. 27)

### 33. Quickbeam or Rowan or Mountain ash *(Sorbus aucuparia* L.*)*

*Antiquity ascribed magical powers to the Quickbeam, utilised by the Druids both for oracular purposes, and as a charm against witches. Its berries were considered "food of the gods" - i.e. forbidden food, probably in extension of the ban on eating the scarlet toadstools which produced (supposedly inspired) delirium. In ancient Greece all red foods such as lobster, bacon, red mullet, crayfish, scarlet berries and fruit were taboo except at feasts honouring the dead.*

This slender medium-sized deciduous tree grows up to heights of 5 m. Its pinnate leaves consist of 11-21 separate serrated folioles. The snow-

1 *Service tree*   2, 3 *Wild service tree*   4, 5 *Quickbeam*

white flowers, which are very small and 5-petalled, grow umbeliferously at the branch terminals, developing into scarlet red berries almost 1 cm across. The drupes remain on the tree during the winter and are a valuable source of food for birds. Rowan, with brilliantly gold foliage in the autumn, flourishes in the deciduous forests of northern Greece, alongside other woodland trees. (For description of genus see p. 27)

### 34. Whitebeam *(Sorbus aria* (L.) Crantz*)*

This medium-sized deciduous tree has a domed crown of simple, obovate dark-green leaves, shiny above and silvery, densely pubescent below. The small white flowers grow in a loose umbel, developing into scarlet round or oval drupes, each containing several seeds. Whitebeam grows in mountain locations in mainland Greece and on Crete, standing singly in wood - or pasture land. It particularly likes soils rich in lime. (For description of genus see p. 27)

### 35. Balkan Whitebeam *(Sorbus umbellata* L.*)*

This deciduous shrub or small tree is similar to the above *(q.v.)* but has smaller leaves, deeply divided into toothed lobes and with 4-7 pairs of parallel veins. The round drupes are yellowish brown, about 1.5 cm in diameter. (For description of genus see p. 27)

**False medlar** *(Sorbus chamaemespilus)* is not a member of the genus *Mespilus* at all, and grows as a compact shrub of about 50 cm to 1 m high. The unequally toothed leaves are elliptical, the radial flowers dark pink and borne in dense umbels. The pea-sized fruit is small and orange. In Greece this plant is found only on Mt Athos. (For description of genus see p. 27)

**1, 2** *Whitebeam*    **3, 4** *Balkan Whitebeam*

# Plums

**36. Greek plum** *(Prunus pseudarmeniaca* Heldr. and Sart.)

Whether growing as a large bush or as a tree, this wild plum has a spherical crown of deciduous foliage, with elliptical leaves carried on dense branches. The white 5-petalled flowers grow in twos in the leaf axils. The paired, round fruit is a pale yellow; it has an aromatic smell, and despite its somewhat acid taste is much sought after by the country people. Greek plum grows on the mountainsides in mainland Greece and in the Peloponnese. (For description of genus see p. 27)

**37. Macedonian plum** *(Prunus cerasifera s.sp. divaricata* schneid.*)*

A deciduous tree resembling Greek plum *(q. v.)*, this species has larger leaves, the veins of which are outlined with hair. Also, the fruit is carried on longer stalks, is golden and larger in size than that of Greek plum, but has the same acidity. A subspecies sports red fruit. As its name suggests, Macedonian plum grows in northern Greece. (For description of genus see p. 27)

**38. Wild plum** *(Prunus domestica* L. s.sp. *instititia* Schneide*)*

The leaves of this small deciduous tree are pubescent on the underside. The typical white, 5-petalled flowers usually appear in pairs. The fruit, a round fleshy drupe, is yellow or rusty-red in colour. *P. instititia* grows in mountain forests all over Greece, and is the common ancestor of all cultivated varieties of plum and prune. Indeed, saplings growing here and there from scattered seeds of the cultivated species tend to create a confusion, as it is very difficult to distinguish between the cultivated and the truly wild tree. (For description of genus see p. 27)

**1, 2** *Greek plum*     **3** *Macedonian plum*     **4, 5, 6** *Wild plum*

69

### 39. Blackthorn or Sloe *(Prunus spinosa L.)*

This low deciduous tree-grows to only about 2 m or so. The limbs are twisted, and the thorny branches form a complicated, far from compact crown. The small simple leaves are elliptical and dentate. The small flowers, about 1.5 cm across, have 5 creamy-white petals, and grow axillary, rather densely clustered. The fruits are small, round, fleshy, blue-black drupes with a whitish bloom, extremely astringent. The species is common to scrubland and forests of mainland Greece. The famous Yugoslav slivovitz brandy is made from fermented sloes. (For description of genus see p. 27)

## Cherries

### 40. Wild or Bird cherry *(Prunus avium (L.) L.)*

This quite large deciduous tree grows to 25 m in height. The bark is a glossy metallic grey with prominent brown lenticels in horizontal bands. The leaves are oval or oblong, serrated at the edges, and pointed at the tip; they are pubescent on the underside and have fairly long petioles. The flowers grow in clusters of 2-6, each with its own stem. They are about 2 cm across, white, with 5 petals each, and a multitude of golden stamens. The fleshy fruit is usually deep red but occasionally yellow, and has a sweet taste with something of a tang. It hangs down from stalks several cms long, a number of these joined together at the top. This species is the progenitor of all the cultivated varieties of cherry, and will often grow from the discarded seeds of the cultivated fruit. In autumn, the foliage of this tree tinges into brilliant shades of gold and scarlet; in winter, the buds on the twig are a bright reddish brown. Wild cherry is to be found in Greek mountain woodlands at medium altitudes. (For description of genus see p. 27)

### 41. St Lucie's cherry *(Prunus mahaleb L.)*

This small deciduous tree or large bush is up to 12 m tall. The finely-dentate hard leaves measure between 5-8 cm; they are oval or in the shape of an elongated heart, glossy green above and pubescent below. The flowers grow many of them together in erect clusters on long stalks; they are white, with 5 largish petals, and delicately fragrant. The fruit is the size of a large pea, deep-crimson to black, and bitter, and used dried

**1** *Blackthorn*    **2, 3, 4** *Wild cherry*    **5, 6** *St Lucie's cherry*

by confectioners. It is from this species also that cherrywood pipes are made. (For description of genus see p. 27)

**42. Cherry laurel** *Prunus laurocerasus* L.)

This is an evergreen shrub or small tree with large, glossy, leathery, dark green leaves, oval-lanceolate in shape, and with their veins and petioles of a much lighter colour. The small white flowers with a mass of well protruding stamens are carried on long erect spikes at the ends of the branches. They develop into small deep red or purple drupes. *P. laurocerasus* is to be found in Thrace. (For description of genus see p. 27)

All parts of this poisonous plant contain prussic acid, and its crushed leaves have been used by entomologists to kill insects.

Another, very low, shrubby species of prunus to be found in Greece is **P. prostate,** which grows in several stony locations in the mountains.

## Almond and Peach

*In the Thesean age the goddess Artemis, in her aspect of the nymph Phyllis, was metamorphosed into an almond tree. It was also from the almond tree that Aaron took his magic rod, and its budding was reproduced in the almond-shaped sconces of the* menorah, *the seven-branched candlestick of the Jerusalem temple sanctuary.*

**43. Almond** *(Prunus amygdalus* Stokes *Prunus dulcis)*

Both the cultivated and the wild almond, originally introduced from Asia, are very widespread in Greece. They grow from 4-7 m in height, with smooth lanceolate leaves with serrated margins. The wild variety usually has 5-petalled pink flowers with a deeper roseate centre and produces small bitter nuts; on the cultivated tree the flowers are pink or white, and produce sweet edible almonds. The fruit is an oval fleshless drupe, the outer velvety case of which splits open at full maturity to reveal its pale-brown shelled kernel, which in turn contains the almond. The flowers, which appear spectacularly on the bare branches before any leaves have appeared, open as early as February or even January. Almond trees like warm, barren limestone regions over almost all of Greece. (For description of genus see p. 27)

**44. Wild peach** *(Prunus webbii)*

This small deciduous tree or shrub is easily confused with the Wild almond *(q.v.),* but has very narrow leaves, not more than 9 mm in width.

**1, 2** *Cherry laurel*    **3, 4, 5** *Almond*    **6** *Wild peach*

73

The flowers are a deep pink. The hard and tasteless fruits are hard and downy, rather resembling small peaches, and measure about 2-2.5 cm across. This species is common to southern Greece and Crete, where it grows in dry, rocky locations. (For description of genus see p. 27)

# Hawthorns

*In European folklore hawthorn used to be considered an unlucky tree. It was associated with the month of May when it flowers,and is the tree of the goddess Maia (whose son Hermes conducted souls to Hades). Sex too fell under its bane, and May marriages were considered unlucky — and still are in parts of rural Greece. The ancient Greeks thought it prudent to propitiate the goddess Maia, who disliked marriages, with brands of hawthorn wood and hawthorn blossom at the beginning of May.*

### 45. **Woody hawthorn** *(Crataegus laciniata Uch. Crataegus orientalis)*

This deciduous, many -branched spiny shrub grows to 3 m in height. The alternate leaves,carried on long slim petioles,are relatively large and pinnate, with either serrated or smoothly lanceolate lobes and toothed stipules. The little white flowers grow in small domed clusters up to 5 cm across. The fruit, called a haw, is a small red, roundish or oval drupe, much used in herbal remedies. Woody hawthorn grows in the mountain forests of Macedonia and Crete,and possibly elsewhere. (For description of genus see p. 28)

### 46. **Heldreich hawthorn** *(Crataegus heldreichii Boiss)*

A deciduous, spiny shrub of up to 4 m in height, this species has smallish, deeply divided pinnately lobed leaves, serrated towards the tip, carried on short petioles with whole stipules. They are softly pubescent on the underside and almost smooth on top. The flower is characteristic of hawthorn (see description of genus p. 28). The fruit is a red drupe about 1.5 cm across. Heldreich hawthorn can be found on barren soils and high pasture lands almost anywhere in the Greek mountains.

**1, 2, 3** *Woody hawthorn*     **4, 5, 6** *Heldreich hawthorn*

## 47. Common hawthorn *(Crataegus monogyna* Jacq.*)*

This deciduous shrub or small tree of only 2-4 m distinguishes itself by its multitude of thorns. Its light green leaves are sphenoid at the base with toothed stipules, and divide into 3-7. The highly scented, small white flowers with red anthers are carried in dense, flat-topped clusters. Common hawthorn flourishes in scrubland and woodland at medium and low altitudes, mixed in with other shrubs or trees. It is easily found in most of Greece. There are also a large number of subspecies with variations in the shape of the leaf and the pubescence or non-pubescence of the leaf and twig. (For description of genus see p. 28)

## 48. Greek hawthorn *(Crataegus schraderana* Ledeb.*)*

This species, which grows as a deciduous shrub, has slender branches which are pubescent at the tips and otherwise almost smooth, with a reddish bark. It may be sparsely provided with thorns of up to 10 mm in length, or have none at all. The 30-50 mm leaves are oblong or rhomboidal, hairy underneath at first, later also becoming almost smooth. They have 3-5 broad lobes each with 1-3 dentations at the tip. They are borne on short petioles rising from broad stipules with either serrated or whole margins. The white flowers have small, triangular sepals. Each umbel develops into 12-14 deep red haws of 1.5 cm, which have the form of flattened spheres. (For description of genus see p. 28)

## 49. Azarole *(Crataegus azarolus* L.*)*

This member of the hawthorn genus (for description see p. 28) grows as a bush or a small tree of up to 9 m with well-spread limbs; it has few thorns, if any. The leaves are from 3-7 cm long, sphenoid at the base with pinnate, almost wholly separated lobes. The short petioles rise from toothed to ciliated stipules. The white flowers with purple anthers are carried in scattered dense clusters on hairy stalks. The haw is spherical or oval, coloured in varing shades of orange. Azarole has been found mainly in Crete and Rhodes, although it may also grow elsewhere in Greece.

**1, 2, 3** *Common hawthorn*     **4, 5** *Greek hawthorn*     **6** *Azarole*

## 50. Pubescent hawthorn *(Crataegus pycnoloba* Boiss and Heldr.*)*

This is one of the thornier species of the genus (for description see p. 28). Its relatively very small leaves are covered with silvery hairs and deeply divided into separate lobes. The leaf stalk has very small, entire stipules. The tender young shoots and the flower stems are again densely pubescent. The flowers are white and carried in the small bouquets typical of the genus. The fruit is relatively large, round, red, and - to do the name of the plant full justice - also downy with hair. Pubescent hawthorn grows at more elevated altitudes in the Peloponnese and Attica.

## 51. Black hawthorn *(Crataegus pentagyna* Wald and Kit.*)*

This is a large shrub or small tree, up to 5 m in height. The young leaves begin life hairy on their upper side, but later become glabrous. From a sphenoid base they divide into not so very pronounced lobes; the leaf stalk has entire ciliated stipules. The small white flowers, bunched in the typical clusters (for description of the genus see p. 28) and carried on pubescent stalks, have striking red anthers. The fruits are pulpy black drupes - hence the name - and contain 4-5 seeds each. Black hawthorn flourishes in the mountains of northern Greece.


# Wildberries


## 52. Blackberry *(Rubus fruticosus* L.*)*

This large, usually evergreen, rambling shrub, up to 4 m high and with numerous subspecies, has strong triangular thorns. The leaves divide into 3 or 5 elliptical or obovate lobes, are dark green above and greyish on the underside, and prickly along the centre vein. The radial flower has 5 white petals, growing in compound terminal clusters on the long, straight branches and from stiff short sidebranches. The well-known juicy fruit changes from green to red and finally to purplish black in the ripening process. It has numerous one-seeded fleshy carpels on a pithy core. Blackberries grow all over Greece as thickets and hedges, for preference in sunny locations at low altitudes. (For description of genus see p. 28)

Home-brewed blackberry wine, made from the fermented fruit, is a light but heady drink. Blackberry leaves make a medicinal herbal tea.


**1** *Pubescent hawthorn*     **2** *Black hawthorn*     **3, 4, 5** *Blackberry*

### 53. **Yellowberry** *(Rubus tomentosus* Borck)*

This bushy shrub seldom reaches the size of Blackberry described above. Its slim branches are studded with small, scythe-shaped thorns. The leaves are velvet-soft with downy hairs, and whitish on the underside. They divide into 3-5 lobes, with the central leader larger than the others, and are carried on long petioles with 2 small stipules at their base. The cream-coloured radial flowers, which give the plant its name, grow in compound clusters and develop into round black berries typical of the genus (for description see p. 28). This is a common species, easily found in the Greek *maquis*.

### 54. **Raspberry** *(Rubus idaeus* L.)*

This species grows as a suckering shrub with many straight shoots reaching up to 2 m in height, and covered all the way up in needle-thin hard prickles. The pinnate leaf, a light greyish-green on the underside and densely pubescent, is carried on a long petiole and divides into 3-7 long-pointed folioles. At the base of the leaf stalk are two small whispy stipules. The white radial flowers have 5 widely-spaced lanceolate petals, and grow in dense clusters on lateral shoots. The well-known raspberry resembles the blackberry *(q.v.)* in shape, but is rather more oval, "raspberry red", and softer to the palate on account of its very fine downy hairs. The species is cultivated outside Greece specifically for its fruit. In Greece itself it is only found growing wild, in high-altitude woodland forests or in stony locations in the mountainous areas of the North. (For description of genus see p. 28)

### 55. **Woodberry** *(Rubus thyrsoides* Wimm.)*

This medium-sized shrub with pendant, arching branches is supplied with moderately large spines. The leaves are 5-lobed and pubescent on the underside. The white or pink radial flowers grow in upright compound clusters, maturing into round black berries. Woodberry grows in the high mountain areas of northern Greece. (For description of genus see p. 28)

### 56. **Mountainberry** *(Rubus hirtus* W. and K.)*

This medium-sized shrub has needle-fine prickles which at first sight appear to be merely a coat of hair. The dark-green foliage consists of hairy and glandular leaves, carried on long petioles with a covering of red

**1** *Yellowberry*   **2, 3** *Raspberry*   **4** *Woodberry*   **5** *Mountainberry*

prickles. Each leaf divides into 3-5 lobes, each on its own short leaf stalk, the central leaflet being oval or heart-shaped. The flowers grow in compound clusters, and the fruit resembles a round, black raspberry. (For description of genus see p. 28)

Another two wildberries found in Greece are too small to be classified as shrubs. They are **Rock bramble** *(R. saxatilis)*, a plant with short, spreading branches, white flowers and small slate-blue fruits, and **Dewberry** *(R.caesius)*, with leaves grey-green on the underside, comparatively large white flowers, and fruits with a purplish bloom.

## Wild Roses

### 57. Evergreen rose *(Rosa sempervirens L.)*

This evergreen climbing shrub grows to a height of 2 m . Its slim long branches like to support themselves up the Kerm oak, the Arbute, or other shrubs of the *maquis* where it is to be principally found. This species has sparse curved thorns, and leaves compoundly pinnate with 5 long-pointed and serrated leaflets; at the base of the petiole are two slender, pointed stipules. The flower corollas are formed by five broad petals, and measure about 5 cm across. The flowers generally grow in pairs on long glandular stems, mostly at the tips of the new branches. As in all roses, the stamens are prominently arranged in a dense ring at the centre of the corolla. Long oval sepals, narrowing to a lanceolate tip, drop off as the seed ripens. The fruit, in the rose genus called a hip, is oval, small and orange when ripe, smooth on the outside and, like all hips, carrying several seeds in its hair-lined interior. (For description of genus see p. 28)

### 58. Field rose *(Rosa arvensis Hudson)*

Up to 2 m in height, this climbing shrub has long slim branches provided with occasional thorns. The compound pinnate leaves, with 5-7 elliptical or oval, serrated leaflets, pubescent on the underside, usually fall during the winter months. The narrow stipules are attached to the petiole for almost their entire length. The white radial flower has 5 petals, measures about 5 cm across, and usually appears singly on slim glandular stems. The sepals are sharply pointed long ovals; they are recurved, and eventually drop off as the fruit ripens. The hip is small, oval, glossy and red. This rose, along with many subspecies, is common all

**1, 2** *Evergreen rose*     **3** *Field rose*

1

2

3

over mainland Greece. It grows freely in woodlands at high altitudes, where it likes to climb up the trunks of trees or shrubs or to trail across the rocks. (For description of genus see p. 28)

### 59. Dog rose (Rosa canina L.)

The commonest of the European wild roses, this large shrub reaches 3 m in height and has long, stout branches with tough, broad-based and recurved thorns. The usually smooth pinnately compound leaf has 5-7 serrated folioles. At the base of the main petiole are two long, narrow pointed stipules, joined together for most of their length. The scentless flowers are usually pink, occasionally white, and rarely grow singly; they generally appear two or three together on short, smooth, glossy stems at the tips of the new shoots. The sepals are pointed, with linear segmentation of the margins, and turn downwards. The good-sized smooth hip is either orange or scarlet in colour. Dog rose too has a great number of subspecies. In antiquity it was much used as a medicinal plant. It is to be commonly found in woods and scrubland all over Greece. (For description of genus see p. 28)

### 60. Rusty rose (Rosa ferruginea Desegl.)

This dense, much-branching 1-2 m tall shrub also has strong, curved thorns. The pinnate leaves, with 5-7 smooth and pointed folioles, are blue-tinged and serrated; they usually bear crimson stigmata. The petiole emerges from between 2 broad stipules. The typical rose flowers (for description of genus see p. 28) are set into large bracts at the ends of the new shoots; they are borne on short stems and are a dusty pink colour. The segmented sepals are erect. The smooth hip is oval or round, and orange. Rusty rose grows in the mountains of central Greece.

**1, 2, 3** Dog rose     **4** Rusty rose

1

2

3                                    4

85

### 61. Mountain rose (Rosa montana Choix.)

This large shrub grows up to 3 m tall and is distinguished by the reddish bark of its branches. The thorns are hardly curved at all, and almost linear. The pinnate leaves, rising from broad stipules, consist of 5-9 folioles, rounded at the tip and, like those of Rusty rose, are usually marked with red stigmata. The pink flowers are borne on longish stems, well clear of the bracts. The linearly segmented sepals stand erect and remain on the fruit until it is completely ripe. The red hip is covered with tough, bristly hairs. Mountain rose is to be found at the higher elevations of the Pindus mountain range. (For description of genus see p. 28)

### 62. Small-flowered rose (Rosa micrantha Sm.)

This shrub of 1-2 m in height is only sparsely foliated. The branches are very long and trail on the ground. The recurved thorns are few and far between. The pinnate leaves have 5-7 glandular and serrated folioles. A hairy, glandular stem supports the small white or pink flowers (for description of genus see p. 28), which grow either several of them together or singly. The sepals drop off before the hip attains full maturity. This species, with many variants, grows in scrubland and in hedges at medium altitudes throughout mainland Greece and on the islands of the Ionian sea.

### 63. Downy rose (Rosa tomentella Lem.)

This light-green shrub growing up to 2 m high has its full complement of sturdy thorns. The leaves, with the typical complement of 5-7 small oval and serrated leaflets (for description of genus see p. 28), are densely pubescent on the underside. The stipules at the petiole base are broader nearer the top of the plant. The flowers, characteristic of the genus, are usually white and grow in groups of several on smooth stems. The sepals are pinnately lobed, recurved, and drop off long before the smooth, red, oval hip has fully ripened. Downy rose is to be found in the *maquis* at medium altitudes in central Greece and the Peloponnese.

**1** *Mountain rose*   **2, 3, 4** *Small-flowered rose*   **5** *Downy rose*

87

#### 64. Shining rose *(Rosa nitidula* Bess.)

The slender reddish branches of this shrub grow up to 2 m long and have distinctive reddish-green leaves and sparse, curved thorns.The pinnate leaves, with 5-7 serrated folioles, are smooth above and pubescent-glandular below; the stipules are short and broad. The flower petals are pink, usually tinged a darker hue around the edges and lighter in the centre. The segmented sepals are recurved. Shining rose is to be found in the Pindus mountain range. (For description of genus see p. 28)

#### 65. Meadow rose *(Rosa agrestis* Savi)

This species, up to 2 m high, has relatively sparse branches which bend towards the ground and are furnished with strong, sickle-shaped thorns. The typical compound leaves (for description of genus see p. 28) have 5-7 leaflets, glandular on the underside. The white flowers are borne singly or in groups of two or more;long sepals show minor segmentation. The hip is oval to spherical, red and smooth, and has cast off the sepals before it is ripe. Meadow rose is to be found in the scrublands of northern Greece.

There are other wild roses in Greece which do not classify as shrubs because of their low height of less than 1 m. They are the brightly carmine-flowered **Alpine rose** *(R.pendulina* L.), which grows in the mountains of northern Greece; sweet-scented **French rose** *(R. gallica* L.),* with pink to purplish flowers, found in the mountain forests and the ancestor of many cultivated species; **Burnet rose** *(R. spinosissima* L.),* with creamy-yellow flowers and extremely densely thorned branches, which grows in stony soils in northern Greece; **Orphanidis rose** *(R. Orphanidea* Boiss and Rent*),* with pink flowers and dense thorns,to be found in the mountains of central Greece and Thessaly; **Heckelian rose** *(R. heckeliana* Tratt*),* with pink flowers and hairy hips,which grows on all the Greek mountains; pink-flowered **Sicilian rose** *(R. sicula* Tratt*)* of stony soils anywhere; and the pink or white **Glandular rose** *(R. glutinosa css),* its branches densely covered with thorns and glandular, hairy leaves.

It is also worth mentioning **Thorny burnet** here *(Sarcopoterium spinosum* (L.) Spach*),*a low, spiny grey-green shrub which never grows

---

**1, 2** *Shining rose*   **3** *Meadow rose*   **4** *A Alpine rose*   *B French rose*   *C Burnet rose*   *D Heckelian rose*   *E Sicilian rose*   *F Glandular rose*   *G Orphanidis rose*

taller than 60 cm. It bears its red, very fleshy berry-like fruit in crowded clusters, and is common throughout Greece.

# Amelanchiers

### 66. Alpine or Snowy mespilus *(Amelanchier ovalis* Med.*)*

This deciduous shrub grows variously from 1-3 m tall. Its simple oval or elliptical leaves, borne on short petioles, are dentate and covered with a film of fine hairs on their underside when young, which they later shed and become smooth. The long-stalked flowers are borne in flat-topped clusters; they are white, with 5 narrow, 1.5-2 cm long petals, pubescent on their underside, and have 5 pointed sepals. The edible fleshy drupe is the size of a pea, blue-black in colour, and sweetish. This species is to be found in the forests covering the mountain slopes in northern Greece. (For description of genus see p. 28)

### 67. Cretan mespilus *(Amelanchier cretica* (Wild) D.C.*)*

This deciduous shrub grows up to 2.5 m tall, having oval or disc-shaped leaves which are whitish and hairy on the underside when young but later become glabrous. The white flowers are smaller than those of Alpine mespilus *(q.v.)*, but grow in the same formation. The pea-sized drupe is again blue-black and edible. This mespilus grows among the rocks anywhere in the alpine zone of mainland Greece and, as its name implies, on Crete. (For description of genus see p. 28)

# Pyracantha - Cotoneaster

### 68. Coral tree or Fire thorn *( Pyracantha coccinea* M.J. Roemer*)*

This thorny, evergreen shrub with densely set branches grows in its natural state to 2 m. in height. The leathery leaves are about 2 cm long grey-green elliptical oblongs. The somewhat unassuming white flowers with 5 petals measure less than 1 cm across. They grow in small white umbels in succeeding leaf axils near the end of the shoots. The conspicuous drupe berries, which ripen in autumn and remain on the wood for quite some while, are the size of a slightly flattened pea and either dark orange or red, each containing 5 small seeds in its fleshy pulp.

**1** *Alpine mespilus*     **2** *Cretan mespilus*     **3** *Coral tree*

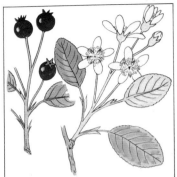

Coral tree grows wild in the forests of northern Greece as far up as Mt Olympus. It is also often planted in parks and city squares for its spectacularly ornamental berry clusters. (For description of genus see p. 29)

Cotoneaster is a close relative of Coral tree, and represented in Greece by two species: (1) **Common cotoneaster** *(Cotoneaster vulgaris),* which grows as a small shrub of up to 1 m , with 5-petalled pink flowers, erect leaves pubescent on the underside, and rosy-red drupes; it can be found on rocky ground in northern Greece, (2) **Tomentose cotoneaster** *(C. tomentosus),* with 5-petalled white or pink flowers, leaves and young shoots densely pubescent, and small red drupes, growing in mainland Greece.


# Plane

*As far back as the time of Ecclesiastes, the plane had long been associated by the Greeks with the pursuit of wisdom. Planes live for hundreds of years and grow to great heights and girths. The island of Cos in the Dodecanese boasts the legendary "plane tree of Hippocrates". Its lower branches are much propped up, but it is a truly venerable specimen.*

**69. Oriental plane** *(Platanus orientalis L.)*

The spreading crown of this large deciduous tree is easily 20 m or more high. The most distinctive feature of this plant is the bark, which flakes off in segments, exposing white wood which turns green and later brown, giving a vividly dappled appearance. The leaves are deeply lobed into 5-7 sections, and each of these may be pointedly subdivided on leaves further down on the tree. The flowers are wind-pollinated, the males resembling catkins, the females, hanging down on long stalks, cluster together in what are aptly called bobbles. As many as 3 or 4 bobbles may hang from the same stalk one below the other. These round heads turn brown as they ripen, break up, and release scores of tiny seeds to be dispersed by the wind. Plane timber, if cut at a tangent to the circumference, reveals an intricate pattern and is sold as "lacewood". Plane trees grow in regions where there is plenty of water, and there are magnificent specimens to be found in Pilion and northern Greece, especially on river banks and in ravines. Given enough water, plane thrives at altitudes from sea-level up

**1, 2** *Coral tree*    **3, 4, 5, 6** *Oriental plane*

to and even above 1,500 m. The bark-shedding, which aids its intake of oxygen, also helps it to survive well in smoke-polluted cities. (For description of genus see p. 29)

**70. Liquidambar** *(Liquidambar orientalis L.)*

This deciduous tree is very similar to plane *(q.v.)* whose leaf and flower pattern it follows closely, except that the flowers have no petals. Liquidambar originated in Asia, and the only place where it can be found self-propagated in Greece is on Rhodes, where it grows particularly in the famous Valley of the Butterflies.

# Carob

**71. Carob** or **Locust tree** *(Ceratonia siliqua L.)*

This medium-sized evergreen tree with dense foliage forming either a rounded or more spreading crown has compound pinnate leaves with 2-5 pairs of folioles, but lacks a terminal leaflet at the end of the main leaf axis. The green petalless flowers are very small and grow in elongated clusters from buds on the old wood. The carob fruit is a pod resembling a broadbean and turns chocolate brown when ripe. It is often used as animal fodder, but the seeds may be ground into flour for human consumption. Carob is a tree of hot regions and thrives in southern Greece and on the islands. It is also frequently grown as an ornamental specimen. The seeds were the original "carat" weights of goldsmiths. (For description of genus see p. 29)

# Bean trefoil

**72. Bean trefoil** *(Anagyris foetida L.)*

With pubescent branches, this shrub or occasionally bushy tree grows about 3 m tall. The compound leaves have 3 separate elliptical folioles and give off a fetid smell when crushed, accounting for the second half of the Latin name. They too are hairy on the underside, but smooth above. The leguminous flowers (for description of genus see p. 29) grow in hanging racemes from the leaf axils, each flower about 2.5 cm long, yellow, with a black blotch at the base of the standard. The fruit pod measures from 10-18 cm, and is swollen down the middle and flat along the seams; the seeds are violet or yellow. Bean trefoil likes dry, stony locations at low altitudes, and grows almost anywhere in Greece. The

**1** *Liquidambar*    **2, 3, 4** *Carobtree*    **5, 6** *Bean trefoil*

whole plant is poisonous and was well known in ancient times as an emetic.

# Laburnum

**73. Laburnum** *(Laburnum anagyroides* Med.)

This small deciduous tree may also grow as a bush, reaching 3-6 m in height. On older specimens the bark, which always remains glossily smooth, takes on a rich olive-green colour. The dark green leaves, carried on long petioles with or without stipules, consist of 3 oval to oblong leaflets of equal size, smooth above and slightly hairy on the underside. The leguminous flowers (for description of genus see p. 29) resemble tiny golden butterflies with fine brown stripes, and hang in racemes of up to 20 cm from the leaf axils. The fruit is a hard brown pod about 5 cm long, narrow at the base and broadening out towards and after the middle, and contains 3-7 neatly round seeds. These, as all parts of the tree, are extremely poisonous, and in times past were used as a purgative. Laburnum is rare as a wild species in Greece, and can only be found in the woods around the village of Pertouli on Mt Koziakas in the Pindus range. Makers of woodwind instruments like laburnum wood for its density, stability and good resonance.

# Spiny Brooms

**74. Great spiny broom** *(Calycotome infesta* Guss*)*

This 1-2 m high shrub has spiny branches with small trifoliate leaves, softly hairy on the underside and smooth above. The yellow flowers are characteristic of the pea family (for description see p. 29) and grow 2-4 of them clustered together in the leaf axils. The fruit is a small oblong pod, covered with short silvery hairs. It has thick seams or narrow seedwings along the sides. Spiny broom is found in scrubland at low altitudes in northern Greece?

Very similar to the above is **Small spiny broom** *(C. villosa)* of southern Greece, but this is considerably smaller (1 m or less) and bears its flowers in groups of more than 4; its pod is hairless.

*Very appropriately, a concoction of broom flowers was Henry VIII's favourite medicine since, strongly diuretic, they had for long been prized as "a remedy against all surfeits".*

**1, 2** *Laburnum*     **3, 4** *Great spiny broom*     **5** *Small spiny broom*

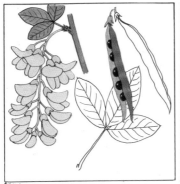

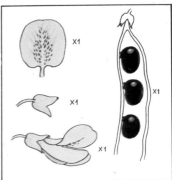

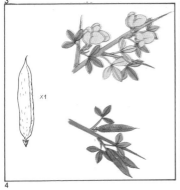

# Black Broom

**75. Black broom** *(Lembotropis nigricans* Griseb.*)*

This small, 1-2 m high shrub carries its branches stiffly erect, and many of the leguminous yellow flowers grow close together on long spikes at the tips of the branches. (For description of flower and genus see p. 29).The wings of the flower are shorter than the keel. The dark-green trifoliate leaves on short petioles are pubescent on the underside. The fruit is a hairy pod about 2-3 cm long. Black broom is rare in Greece, appearing sparsely only in the forested regions of Epirus.

# Brooms

**76. Montpellier broom** *(Cytisus monspessulanus* L.*)*

This shrub attains heights of up to 3 m. The leaves, carried on long petioles and divided into 3 small folioles, are pubescent on the underside. The bright yellow leguminous flowers (for description see p. 29) grow in clusters of 3-9 on the young branches, developing into small pods containing from 4 to 6 seeds. This very decorative species is quite common in forests all over mainland Greece.

**77. Triple- flowered broom** *(Cytisus triflorus* L'Her.*)*

Like Bean trefoil, this 1-2 m high shrub also has its branches covered with hair. The trifoliate leaves divide into 3, equally hairy, obovate folioles. The yellow flowers (for description see p. 29) generally grow in groups of three (hence the plant's name) from the leaf axils, long flower stalks carrying them well clear of the foliage. The hairy pods are about 3-3.5 cm long. This rather pretty species frequents scrublands and low-altitude forests throughout mainland Greece.

The Greek flora also includes other species of *cytisus* of woody growth which, however, due to their small size, can at most be classed as dwarf shrubs. They are the yellow-flowered **Hairy broom** *(C. hirsutus)*, growing no taller than 90 cm; the tiny yellow **Prickly broom** *(C. spinescens)*, which only grows to 15 cm and has branches as unfriendly as its name implies; **Cretan broom** *(C. creticus)*, an equally dwarf, yellow species; **White broom** *(C. albus)* growing up to 1 m, with unusually white flowers; yellow **Thessalian broom** *(C. thessalus)*, up to 30 cm; and the 60 cm high **Rock broom** *(C. supinus)* and **Mountain broom** *(C. medius)* both with markedly spreading branches and yellow flowers.

**1, 2** *Black broom* **3** *Montpellier broom* **4** *Triple-flowered broom* **5** *Spanish broom*

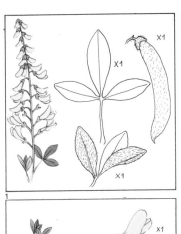

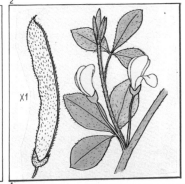

high **Rock broom** *(C. supinus)* and **Mountain broom** *(C. medius)* both with markedly spreading branches and yellow flowers.

## Spanish Broom

**78. Spanish broom** *(Spartium junceum* L.)

The straight, erect, and very smooth branches of this spineless shrub achieve a heitht of 1-3 m, and are very sparsely covered with leaves; there are none at all at the tips, which end in a point, rather like a rush. In very wet years, however, small lanceolate leaves appear sporadically also at these extremes. The characteristic flower (for description see p. 29) is as large as 3 cm, with a prominent erect standard, and has a pleasingly aromatic scent. The slim pod snaps open suddenly when ripe, scattering the seeds over a considerable distance. Spanish broom is one of the most commonly seen shrubs in Greece; it grows wild in the *maquis* at medium altitudes, and planted out along the road sides, either for purely ornamental purposes or to prevent soil erosion.

## Judas Tree

**79. Judas tree** *(Cercis siliquastrum* L.)

This medium-sized tree of up to 10 m, less commonly growing as a bush, has a dense crown of simple leaves which are almost round to kidney-shaped. They are very smooth and a vivid light green in spring, darkening to bluish-green later. The leguminous flowers (for description see p. 29) are up to 2 cm in size and appear just before the leaves; their myriad clusters, a striking pink or rosy mauve, cover the entire length of the branches. The reddish-brown fruit pod is up to 10 cm long. This is quite a common wild tree in Greece, and is also often planted in parks and along avenues for its highly decorative value. Its name derives from the folk belief that Jesus' faithless disciple hanged himself on a tree of this species.

**1, 2** *Spanish broom*    **3, 4, 5** *Judas tree*

# Bladder Sennas

**80. Bladder senna** *(Colutea arborescens* L.)

This deciduous shrub is up to 2 m tall, with pinnate leaves of 7-13 oval folioles. The yellow leguminous flower (for description see p. 29) is about 2 cm long, and grows in erect axillary clusters of 3 to 8. The parchment-like pod is 4-7 cm long, pointed at both ends and greatly swollen out in the middle; it contains many roundish seeds This shrub is a common sight in scrubland at low altitudes almost anywhere in Greece.

**81. Mountain bladder senna** *(Colutea melanocalyx* Boiss and Heldr.*)*

Very similar to the above in appearance and height, this species has leaves with a regular 11 folioles. The flower clusters contain rather fewer individuals than those of Bladder senna, rarely exceeding 6. *C. melanocalyx* grows chiefly in the mountains of northern Greece, but has also been found in the Peloponnese, on Mt Parnos. (For description of genus see p. 29)

# Tree Medick

**82. Tree Medick** *(Medicago arborea* L.)

The leaves of this unusual large shrub fall not in winter like those of other deciduous plants, but at the height of the summer drought. They are trifoliate, with narrow obovate to sphenoid folioles, and have narrow, lanceolate stipules. The small golden leguminous flowers (for description see p. 29) are borne in dense, erect and short-stemmed clusters. The fruit pods are twisted spirally. Tree Medick grows in stony locations in central Greece and the Peloponnese.

# Pomegranate

*Pomegranate was the fruit of which Persephone was tempted to eat a seed when Pluto had abducted her to the underworld, and as a result of having accepted his hospitality to that extent she had to return to him for part of every year — our winter. It was also Saul's sacred tree, and sacred*

**1, 2** *Bladder senna*     **3** *Mountain Bladder senna*     **4, 5** *Tree Medick*

to Tammuz-Adonis from whose blood it is said to have sprung. It was the only fruit permitted inside the Holy of Holies of the Jerusalem Temple, the early Greek pomegranate cult having been assimilated into that of Jehovah.

### 83. Pomegranate *(Pumica granatum L.)*

The self-propagated pomegranate is a large shrub which can reach heights of up to 5 m. It is deciduous with very woody branches, thorny nearer the tips, and oblong glossy leaves with reddish margins on the new shoots. The flower has a large red fleshy calyx which divides at the mouth into 6 red petals spread out in star-fashion, and centred by a veritable tassel of very fine red stamens with yellow anthers. After fertilisation the petals shrivel up, and from the calyx a large, somewhat bumpily spherical fruit develops, ripening to orange brown, deeply crimsoned where the sun reached it. The leathery outer case holds hundreds of seeds, each contained inside a juicy, fleshy pink granule with a very distinctive and refreshing taste. Pomegranate has been cultivated in Greece for its highly-prized fruit since ancient times, and is also found self-propagated on scrubland at the foot of mountains, in ravines, and other generally protected locations. It is particularly common in northern Greece. (For description of genus see p. 30)

# Myrtle

*In antiquity, the evergreen myrtle was sacred all over the Mediterranean to Aphrodite, the love goddess. Also, Greek myth much associated it with the death of kings and resurrection to life after death. Greek emigrants leaving to found a new maritime colony abroad used to carry myrtle boughs, implying: "The old cycle is ended, let us begin a new one, protected by the love goddess who sprang from the sea."*

### 84. Myrtle *(Myrtus communis L.)*

This evergreen shrub, 1-3 m tall, has a very characteristic scent, delicately aromatic. Its thick, glossy leaves grow in opposite pairs, and are lanceolate to oval, pointed at the ends. The branches are straight and grow densely together. The white flowers, with 5 petals and a great many long stamens, appear singly on long stalks from the leaf axil. The small, olive-shaped berry is usually black but occasionally white, and contains a large number of seeds. Myrtle is very common in scrublands at the foot of

**1, 2, 3** *Pomegranate*     **4, 5** *Myrtle*

the mountains, preferring shady places, ravines, or wherever it can find water during the heat of the summer. (For description of genus see p. 30)

# Oleaster

## 85. Oleaster *(Elaeagnus angustifolius* L.)

This medium-sized tree of at most 12 m has branches silvery at the tip when young, and tinged with red in maturity. The leaf is long and thin, grey-green above and silvery scaly on the underside. The small stemless flower, growing axillary, has no petals; its tubular or bell-shaped calyx, which is yellow inside and silvery outside, splits into four at the mouth with recurved tips. When it blossoms in spring, oleaster saturates all the air around with its beautiful scent. The fruits are like olives in size and shape, coloured orange or light brown, and with a sweet mealy pulp pleasant to the taste; in their dried form they are known as Trebizond grapes. Oleaster grows almost anywhere in Greece where there is water: on the banks of streams and waterfalls, in river silt and, since it seems to like salt, especially on sandy beaches very close to the shore. It is often cultivated in gardens and orchards for its fruit, as well as for the fragrance of its blossoms. (For description of the genus see p. 30)

# Cistus

*All the members of this genus are delicately scented. Cistus has been valued since antiquity for its pharmaceutical and aromatic properties, particularly Cretan cistus which yields the resin ladanum.*

## 86. Laurel-leaved cistus *(Cistus laurifolius* L.)

The lanceolate leaves of this 1.5 m high evergreen shrub somewhat resemble those of the laurel, but are very sticky above and grey and woolly-haired on the underside. They grow several one above the other in clusters on the branch terminals, and resemble those of wild rose (for description of the genus *cistus* see p. 30). The 5 white petals of the flower corolla surround a central stigma densely ringed with short yellow stamens. The fruit is a hairy, 5-celled capsule. A rare plant in the Greek flora, *C. laurifolius* exists only in the forests of Thrace.

Other species of cistus to be found in Greece are: **Cretan cistus** *C. villosus)* with large, pinkish flowers; the crinkly **Sage-leaved cistus** *(C. salvifolius)* with large white flowers; **Small-flowered cistus** *(C.*

**1, 2, 3, 4** *Oleaster*     **5** *Laurel-leaved cistus*

*parviflorus)* with medium-sized pink flowers; and **Narrow-leaved cistus** *(C. monspelliensis)* with small white flowers. All of these are low plants, never growing even to 1 m in height.

# Limes

*The pale-green tender new leaves of the lime or linden may be eaten as salads when they first appear, though later they darken and toughen. The flowers make a delicately flavoured honey, and may be dried to be used as a mildly soporific tea with which Greek country mothers try to quieten their babies. Lime wood, very stable and workable, is well liked by wood carvers.*

### 87. Small-leaved lime or Linden *(Tilia cordata* Miller)

This is a large deciduous tree of up to 30 m, with heartshaped and dentate leaves, 5-7 cm across, pointed at the tip, deep green and smooth above when mature, and a lighter green on the underside; they are carried on long petioles. The flowers are borne uncharacteristically upright (for description of genus see p. 30) in groups of 5-11 on a common long stalk, which for about half its length is joined to the lower portion of a long, thin "key" membrane. The flowers are that yellowish-green known as lime green, and have a multitude of stamens. The ripe fruit is a small, dark brown sphere with a brittle shell. Small-leaved lime grows well in the highlands of northern Greece.

### 88. Broad-leaved lime *(Tilia platyphyllos* Scop.)

This densely foliated deciduous tree grows up to 40 m tall. Its heartshaped leaves measure 7-10 cm across, and are quite smooth and a normal green colour on the upper side, but lighter green and slightly pubescent below. The flowers (for description of genus see p. 30) are paler in colour and bigger than those of *T. cordata (q.v.)*, and hang in lax clusters of 2-5. They develop into oval fruits with tough husks. Broad-leaved lime grows in the forests of all of mainland Greece, especially in the more northerly parts of the country.

**1, 2, 3** *Small-leaved lime*    **4, 5, 6** *Broad-leaved lime*

### 89. Silver lime *(Tilia tomentosa* Moench*)*

This up to 30 m high deciduous tree has the usual heartshaped leaves 5-7 cm across (for description of the genus see p. 30). They are slightly hairy on top, and thickly downy and very much lighter on the underside; the twigs and buds are equally pubescent. The two greens of the leaves create a beautiful contrast, especially when the wind stirs the branches, and has given this tree its name. The lime green flowers hang down in pubescent clusters of 7-10. The fruit is elliptical, again hairy, and covered with a hard, woody skin. Silver lime grows in the highland mountains all over mainland Greece, and especially in the northern parts.

# Maples

### 90. Norway maple *(Acer platanoides* L.*)*

A very large deciduous tree, this species can easily reach heights of 30 m and more. The palmately compound, elegantly pointed leaves are large and shiny. The flowers grow in atypically upright short-branched clusters from large reddish bracts at the tips of the twigs, and open just before the leaves; they are quite small and golden green in colour. From the two styles of the ovary develop the greenish twin fruits, joined at the centre and attached to a broad bladed membraneous wing each, pointing in opposite directions like the blades of a propellor. When they are mature they drop off and are carried away by the wind, the seedwings turning in rapid circles. The younger twigs of this species contain a milky sap. Norway maple flourishes on the mountains throughout mainland Greece and the Peloponnese. (For description of the genus see p. 31)

**1, 2, 3, 4** *Silver lime*    **5, 6** *Norway maple*

## 91. Sycamore or Great maple *(Acer pseudoplatanus* L.*)*

This is a large deciduous tree, up to 25 m tall. Its palmate leaves, measuring 8-17 cm across, are set in opposite pairs on long petioles; they are dark green above, and lighter on the underside. The small, pubescent greenish flowers appear in spring on drooping corymbs. The paired winged seeds, pinkish green at first, mature to greenish brown in autumn; the two wings are set roughly at 90°. (For description of genus p. 31). Sycamore flourishes in the mountains of northern Greece as far up as Thessaly. Its timber is the wood always used for the back, sides, and stocks of all string instruments, though their belly must be of spruce.

## 92. Heldreich or Greek maple *(Acer heldreichii* Orph.*)*

This large, up to 25 m high decidous tree carries a dense, neatly rounded crown on a straight trunk with shiny grey bark. Its large leaves, glossy above and pubescent on the underside, are deeply divided into 3 lobes, the central one larger and sphenoid, the outer two each subdivided into two smaller parts at the lower edge. The small, lime-green flowers appear in spring together with the leaves, and are carried in an upright corymb. The paired hairy seeds have their seedwings set at an acute angle. (For description of genus see p. 31). This species usually stands singly among other deciduous trees, and is met with in the forests of northern Greece. It is also planted for ornamental purposes (ripe seedwings are orange, mature petioles red) and for shade in city recreational areas and village squares.

## 93. Balkan maple *(Acer serbicum* Pax. or *A. hyrcanum* F.and M.*)*

This is a smaller, slenderer maple (for description of genus see p. 31), with glossy leaves measuring no more than 8 cm and carried on long petioles. Their shape varies considerably as to number of lobes (3 or 5) and depth of indentation between them. Generally speaking, the leaves divide into 5 more or less projecting sections; their margins are irregularly toothed. The lime green flowers appear in spring and hang in branched clusters. Both flower and fruit are glabrous. The reddish seedwings are steeply angled. Serbian maple grows in northern Greece as far up as Thessaly in the upper and mediate highland belt, usually standing singly among other species. (For description of genus see p. 31)

**1, 2, 3** *Sycamore*    **4, 5** *Heldreich maple*    **6** *Balkan maple*

113

#### 94. **Common** or **Field maple** *(Acer campestre L.)*

This medium-sized deciduous tree never grows taller than 15 m, and is usually found much smaller. The light grey bark is thick, rough and corky. The relatively small leaves measure 7 cm across at the most; they are dark green in colour, shiny above and fuzzy below, set on long, reddish petioles. Their shape varies from one tree to another. (For description of genus see p. 31). In its typical form the leaf divides into 5 lobes; in another variety the leaf has 3 major lobes, each deeply indented again to form 3-5 small pseudo-lobes; finally there is the triple-lobed variety of much plainer outline, and with the lobes pointing more steeply upwards. The small limegreen flowers come out in spring at the extreme tips of the branches, carried in erect, loosely-branched clusters densely covered with hair. The paired, winged seeds are usually pubescent, the wings set in a long straight line exactly opposite each other. Field maple grows in semi-highland and highland zones anywhere in mainland Greece, usually mixed in with other trees.

#### 95. **Amalias maple** *(Acer reginae amaliae Orph.)*

This small species of maple has tough-skinned shiny dark green leaves with a lighter-coloured underside, measuring up to 4 cm across. The pubescent greenish flowers in upright loosely-branched clusters come out together with the leaves. The seeds are unusual in that the wings are set very closely together, lying parallel alongside each other. Amalias maple grows in the highland belt of north-central Greece, mixed in with other trees, and is especially to be found in fir forests. (For description of genus see p. 31)

#### 96. **Montpellier maple** *(Acer monspessulanum L.)*

This is one of the smallest of the maples, the tree attaining only 7 m in height. The relatively small, palmate leaves are neatly 3-lobed. The lime green flowers, borne in upright, long-branched, open clusters, appear at the same time as the young leaves. The seeds are typically paired and winged (for description of genus see p. 31), the wings themselves being reddish and set closely together, though not as closely as in the Amalias maple *(q. v.)*. *A. monspessulanum* is found growing among other forest trees, especially in northern Greece.

**1** *Common maple* **2** *Varieties of the leaves of Common maple* **3** *Common maple* **4** *Amalias maple* **5** *Upper line: Amalias maple-Lower line: Montpellier maple* **6** *Montpellier maple*

### 97. Cretan maple *(Acer creticum* L. *Acer orientale* Tourn.)*

This species, with rather more contorted trunk and less upright limbs, grows as a small tree or in the form of a large bush. It is the only evergreen maple to be found in Greece, keeping its foliage all through the year. Its hard, leathery leaves, divided into 3 lobes, are more compact and have less horizontal spread than those of other maples. The lime green flowers appear April or May in drooping, loosely-branched clusters. The seeds are glabrous, and the wings, usually reddish, steeply angled towards one another. This species is met with in the forests of northern Greece, the Peloponnese, Crete, and the Aegean islands, but also at lower altitudes among the broad-leaved shrubs. (For description of genus see p. 31)

### 98. Obtuse maple *(Acer obtusatum* Kit.)*

This small, straight-limbed, deciduous tree has leaves as large as 10 cm across, pubescent below, and shallowly divided into 5 blunt lobes. A subspecies with pointed lobes can also be found but is rare. When the typical maple flowers (for description of genus see p. 31) come out in branched clusters in spring, they are at first borne upright but droop later; they are lime green in colour and glabrous. The typical winged seed however, is pubescent, and the two wings set at a right angle to each other. Obtuse maple is found in the highland forests of Macedonia and Thrace.

### 99. Tatarian maple *(Acer tataricum* L.)*

Having a rather short trunk relative to its height of up to 7 m, this small deciduous tree could also be described as a large shrub. Its medium-sized leaves are virtually simple, ovoid, and serrated. The atypically white flower comes out in spring, growing in erect clusters at the branch terminals. The elegantly curved wings of the paired seeds are set at a markedly obtuse angle and red. Tatarian maple is a rare species in Greece, found only in certain parts of Macedonia. (For description of genus see p. 31)

**1, 2, 3** *Cretan maple*     **4, 5** *Obtuse maple*     **6** *Tatarian maple*

# Horse Chestnut

**100. Horse chestnut** *(Aesculus hippocastanum* L.*)*

This tree bears no botanical relation to the Sweet chestnut *(Castanea sativa)*, but owes its name in part to the similarity between the fruits of the two trees, and in part to the fact that the nuts of *Aesculus hippocastanum* used to be fed by the Turks to broken-winded horses. Horse chestnut, with a broad and often spirally buttressed trunk, grows to 20 m and more, carrying a large, densely foliated, domed crown. The leaves emerge from fat, sticky brown buds, and are coated in golden-brown downy hairs when they first break through. Their strongly palmate pattern is made up of 5-7 sphenoid folioles spreading out from the top of a common petiole. The flowers, which appear terminally in late spring, grow in conical upright spikes popularly called candles. Each main stalk carries about 15 separate, short-stalked white blossoms with a rusty-red "honey-spot" at their centre to attract insects. The petals of the corolla are uneven in size, those lower down being larger. The fruit ripens in late autumn, with 1 or sometimes 2 chestnuts encased in the pith of a thick, leathery green husk with brown spines. The nuts are very glossy dark brown with a sharply contrasting paler patch, earning the tree its American name of Buckeye. Introduced into Europe from the Balkans in the 17th century, Horse chestnut has since been widely grown as an ornamental tree. Self-propagated specimens are found in Greece only in the forests of the Pindus and Olympus range. (For description of genus see p. 31)

# Terebinths

**101. Turpentine tree** *(Pistacia terebinthus* L.*)*

This much-branching species is usually found in a bushy form, though in full maturity it has the shape of a short-boled tree of up to 5 m. Its leaves are pinnately compound with 7-13 folioles, shiny above and a dull grey-green on the underside. The tiny, rusty-pink flowers (for description of genus see p. 31) appear in spring at the same time as the first leaves, and are densely massed in clusters which at first are borne

**1, 2, 3, 4** *Horse chestnut*     **5** *Turpentine tree*

upright, drooping under their own weight as the fruit develops. The fruits are little nuts the size of small peas, encased in very hard, smooth, rusty-red shells. Many of them massed together in large bunches, they are extremely decorative among the foliage. The gnarled and twisted turpentine tree is a common sight in southern Greece and the Aegean islands, where it grows in the *maquis* alongside other woody shrubs or small trees.

### 102. Macedonian terebinth *(Pistacia mutica* Fisch and Mey.)

This tree is similar to *P. terebinthus* above *(q. v.),* but taller, growing up to 12 m in height. The typical leaves (for description of genus see p. 31) have 3-9 folioles, pubescent on the underside. The case enclosing the ripe nut is black in colour. Macedonian terebinth is met with in scrublands at the bottom of mountains in northern Greece.

### 103. Palestinian terebinth *(Pistacia palaestina* L.)

This rather massive deciduous tree of up to 20 m in height has a broad, thick trunk, which in advanced age can measure more than 1 m in diameter. The typical pinnate leaves (for description of genus see p. 31) have more than 9 leaflets each, dark green above and lighter on the underside. The small fruit cases turn from orange to pink to violet in colour as they ripen. The nut of *P. palaestina* is the popular *tsikouda* which, salted and roasted, is much eaten in Greece. It also yields a viscous, aromatic oil which, though edible, is mostly used medicinally. The tender spring shoots of the tree are often cut and pickled. *P. palaestina* is frequently grafted on to stocks of the pistachio tree, which belongs to the same genus but is not selfpropagating in Greece. Palestinian terebinth is found on Chios, Crete, and other Aegean islands, as well as in Pilion, Euboea and elsewhere.

### 104. Mastic tree *(Pistacia lentiscus* L.)

This is an evergreen shrub, densely foliated, growing 1-6 m tall, with the entire plant giving off a strong scent of resin. The dark green leaves (for description of genus see p. 31) have many leathery narrow folioles. The very small, bell-shaped flowers grow in dense and blunt-topped

**1** *Macedonian terebinth*    **2, 3** *Palestinian terebinth*    **4, 5** *Mastic tree*

spikes from the leaf axils. The fruit is spherical, about 5 mm in diameter and red, later turning black, and makes very prettily decorative clusters. Mastic tree grows in the driest and warmest parts of the *maquis* and along the seashore. It is a species common all over Greece, with a subspecies yielding the famous Chian mastic used in dentistry, medicine, and in ancient times as chewing gum.

## Cotinus

**105. Wig** or **Cloud** or **Smoke tree** (*Rhus cotinus* L. *Cotinus coggygria* Scop.)

This common deciduous shrub grows 2-4 m tall. Its simple leaves, obovate or disc-shaped (for description of genus see p. 31), turn a striking red in autumn. The pink or creamy flowers are minute, carried on relatively long individual stalks in pyramidal clusters, looking like candyfloss. The flowers themselves are sterile, but the spreading hairs which later develop on the flower stalks create the diaphanous grey clusters which have earned the shrub its common names. The species grows in low-altitude scrubland pretty well all over Greece.

**106. Sumach** (*Rhus coriaria* L.)

This low deciduous shrub with milky sap only reaches 1-3 m in height. Its compound leaves (for description of genus see p. 31) divide into 15 pubescent leaflets. The small, greenish-white flowers grow in dense, erect, elongated clusters. The small spherical fruit, purplish-brown and woolly-haired, ripens in tight bunches at the end of the summer. Sumach grows in scrubland at low and medium altitudes almost anywhere in Greece. Dried and ground sumach leaves have long been used for tanning and dying.

**1, 2** *Wig tree*    **3** *Sumach*

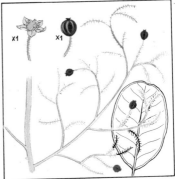

# Holly

*Holly means "holy", and "of all the trees that are in the wood, the holly bears the crown". This is a reference to Jesus, with aspects of whose birth and passion the carol equates each property of the holly. In mythology it is closely associated with the Kerm oak (q.v.) and midsummer oak-king rituals. A giant holly bush was the club of the original Green Knight of Arthurian legend.*

**107. Holly** *(Ilex aquifolium L.)*

This small evergreen tree with tough, dark green leaves is well known as a Christmas decoration. The waxy foliage will burn fiercely, even on the living tree. The trunk is invariably smooth and grey. The leaves are pointed ovals, on the lower branches with sharp broad prickles along the margins as a protection against browsing animals, at the top simple pointed ovals. The small white flowers (for description of genus see p. 32) come out in spring, growing in axillary clusters of many individuals. They ripen into round, brightly red berries about 1 cm across by the beginning of the winter. These drupes hold hard, black seeds packed in yellow pulp. Holly wood is often used for chessmen and, dyed black, as a good substitute for ebony. In many Greek highland villages holly is cultivated as an ornamental shrub. It is found selfpropagated in the Pindus and Orthry ranges of Thrace and Macedonia, where it has formed extensive groves.

# Spindle Trees

*The spindle tree derives its name from the age-long use of its stems as spindles for the hand-spinning of wool (by women known as spinsters), because it is particularly smooth and kind to the fingers. Folklore usage derives a powerful purgative from the pulp of the seeds, as well as yellow dye from the fruit pulp and red dye from the pink husks. Stewed, the fruits give a shining hair-rinse, dried and powdered they kill lice.*

**108. Broad-leaved spindle tree** *(Euonymus latifolius (L.) Miller)*

This graceful deciduous shrub or small tree grows to 6 m or so, with a trunk of smooth, grey bark which eventually develops pink-tinged fissures. The opposite leaves are 7-15 cm long and obovate, with serrated

**1, 2, 3** *Holly*     **4** *Broad-leaved spindle tree*

margins. The orange-yellow flowers (for description of genus see p. 32) are carried in lax, branched axillary clusters with long stalks. The hard-shelled fruit is green at first, later becomes bright pink and expands, the joints of its 5 lobes splitting to reveal 5 seeds clad in orange pulp. At this point the seeds look like tiny lanterns. The high decorative value of this tree is the reason that in the more northerly regions of Greece it is much cultivated in city recreational areas. Self-propagated it grows in mountain forests in northern Greece, very rarely as far south as the Peloponnese.

### 109. Rough-stemmed spindle tree *(Euonymus verrucosus Scop.)*

This low deciduous shrub is only up to 2 m high, with pointedly lanceolate leaves 7 cm in length. (For description of genus see p. 32). It has small, coppery green flowers arranged like those of *E. latifolius (q.v.)*, and beautifully reddish fruits which,when they split open, are seen to contain two-coloured black and orange seeds. This species is to be found in the mountain forests of the North.

### 110. European spindle tree *(Euonymus europaeus L.)*

This very attractive deciduous shrub (for description of genus see p. 32) growing up to 6 m in height has simple opposite leaves, elliptical and pointed. The greenish flowers, with 4 petals twice as long as they are broad, precede pink fruits with four seed lobes. In all respects this species is very similar to *E. latifolius (q. v.)*, but grows more slowly and has smaller flowers and fruit. It can grow pretty well anywhere in mainland Greece, but is more often found in the northern regions.

## Buckthorns

### 111. Field buckthorn *(Rhamnus rupestris Scop.)*

This small tree or shrub of up to 5 m has hard, simple leaves, oval and serrated. (For description of genus see p. 32). The fruits are rather large black drupes. The branches and twigs are covered all over with a sticky excretion. In the Roumeliote subspecies *(rumeliacus)* they are hairy as far up as the leaves. *R. rupestris* grows on rocky ground anywhere in mainland Greece.

**1** *Rough-stemmed spindle tree*    **2** *European spindle tree*    **3** *Field buckthorn*

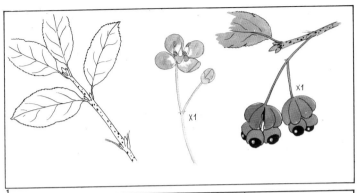

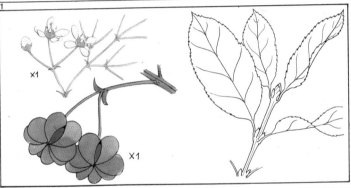

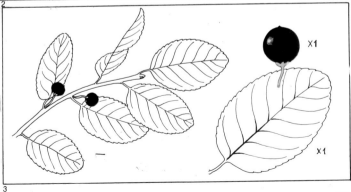

### 112. Alder buckthorn *(Rhamnus frangula L.)*

A smaller tree of the buckthorn genus (for description see p. 32), only 1-4 m in height, this species has simple elliptical leaves with rudimentary stipules. The small greenish flowers grow in sparse clusters in the leaf axils on young wood. The pea-sized drupe changes from green to red to deep violet black. Alder buckthorn flourishes in the mountains of mainland Greece. Its leaves are the favourite food of the caterpillars of the bright yellow brimstone butterfly, and its branches make excellent drawing charcoal.

### 113. Parnassian buckthorn *(Rhamnus guicciardi Heldr. and Sart.)*

This is a small deciduous shrub with leaves elliptical to oblong, somewhat heart-shaped at the base and narrowing towards the top. The fruit is a black drupe. As its name implies, this species is particularly to be found on the higher slopes of Mt Parnassus, but very likely grows on other mountains also. (For description of genus see p. 32)

### 114. Sibthorp buckthorn *(Rhamnus sibthorpianus Roem and Schult)*

An oddity of this member of the genus buckthorn (for description see p. 32) is that some plants bear only fertile female flowers, others only infertile male. They are both densely pubescent, whereas the resulting drupe is quite smooth. The simple leaves are elliptical, 5-7 cm long. Sibthorp buckthorn grows among the rocks at alpine altitudes on all the mountains of mainland Greece.

### 115. Common buckthorn *(Rhamnus catharticus L.)*

The branches of this bushy species (for description of genus see p. 32), which grow up to 4 m, are spreading, thorny, and have relatively dark-coloured leaves. The small, greenish flowers grow in axillary bunches on the old branches. The fruits are spherical black drupes about 1 cm in diameter, and very poisonous; they have been used in veterinary treatment and medically. The species is very common in the Peloponnese and the seven islands of the Ionian Sea.

**1, 2** *Alder buckthorn*   **3** *Panrassian buckthorn*   **4** *Sibthorp buckthorn*
**5,6** *Common buckthorn*

**116. Great-leaved buckthorn** *(Rhamnus fallax* Boiss)

This up to 3 m high shrub has relatively large leaves, 7-13 cm long, elliptoid or obovate in shape. The drupe changes from red to black as it matures. *R. fallax* grows at high altitudes in the mountains of mainland Greece. (For description of genus see p. 32)

**117. Mediterranean buckthorn** *(Rhamnus alaternus* L.)

This is a low, evergreen, erect shrub also growing as a tree, 1-6 m high. Its tough, leathery leaves are elliptical or lanceolate. The yellowish flowers are small and either male or female on any one plant. They lack petals; the calyx develops into the cover for the fruit, a drupe which turns from red to black as it ripens. *R. alaternus* prefers soils rich in lime, and is to be met with in scrubland at low altitudes pretty well throughout Greece. (For description of genus see p. 32)

There are three other species of buckthorn in Greece, prickly dwarf shrubs usually less than 1 m in height. They are **Greek buckthorn** *(R. graecus)* with very small leaves of up to 1.5 cm and rusty-red fruits, which grows in dry regions all over the country; **Plum-leaved buckthorn** *(R. prunifolia)* with leaves up to 12 cm long and hard, brownish-black drupes, which is found on rocky mountains from Macedonia to Crete; and **Olive-leaved buckthorn** *(R. oleoides)* with small lanceolate leaves and chestnut-brown fruits, growing in the islands and southern Greece in dry, rocky locations.

# Cornel Trees

**118. Cornel tree** or **Cornelian cherry** *(Cornus mas* L.)

This small to medium-sized deciduous tree attains up to 7 m in height. The opposite leaves are broadly elliptical and pointed, with characteristic parallel veins. (For description of genus see p. 32). The small, rather yellow flowers, with a recurved, cruciform corolla and four conspicuous stamens, emerge from greyish bracts early in spring before the leaves have appeared, and form noticeable, tightly rounded umbels on the bare branches. The fruit, known as the cornelian cherry, is red and

**1** *Great-leaved buckthorn*     **2, 3, 4** *Mediterranean buckthorn*     **5, 6** *Cornel tree*

fleshy and has an acid tang. Several of them tend to grow together on short stems. Cornel tree can be found all over mainland Greece, but is most common in the mountains of the Pindus range in Macedonia and Thrace.

### 119. Dogwood *(Cornus sanguineus* L.*)*

This deciduous species (for description of genus see p. 32) is generally of bushy growth, but at an advanced age may take the form of a small tree. The bark on the branches has a reddish tint, contrasting well with the green leaves which are softly pubescent on the underside. The cruciform white flowers grow in tight, flat-topped, long-stalked umbels on the branch terminals. The black fruit is round and marked with an "eye". Dogwood flourishes in northern Greece, mixed in with other trees and shrubs.

# Birch

*The birch tree, because of its highly self-propagating characteristic, was in ancient times considered the tree of inception and birth. In parallel, birch twigs were used throughout Europe for ritual floggings (in Scandinavian saunas for reasons of health; more generally to expel evil spirits from lunatics), or to drive out the old year. In this last sense the Roman lictors used to carry birch rods at the installation of new consuls.*

### 120. Silver birch *(Betula pendula* Roth.*)*

This tall deciduous tree has a slim, single or multiple trunk with greyish white bark and long slim branches, the smaller and younger of which usually droop downwards gracefully. The alternate leaves, borne on long petioles, are rhomboidal with deeply serrated margins and neatly parallel veins. The flowers, visible from the previous winter onwards as brown, sausage-like structures, expand in spring and hang down as catkins or "lambs' tails". Some are only male, containing copious amounts of yellow pollen, others only female and greener. The fertile catkins consist of successive layers of membraneous scales, each concealing one ovary. The tiny seeds have each its own papery wing on

**1, 2, 3** *Dogwood*     **4, 5** *Silver birch*

133

which they are dispersed at full maturity .(For description of genus see p. 32). Silver birch is exclusively a tree of cooler climates, and self-propagates in Greece only in the north, in the Rhodopi mountain range close to the border.

# Filberts

*In ancient European folklore the hazel was the tree of wisdom, and in the Mediterranean sacred to Hermes-Mercury, the god of eloquence and intelligence. Hazel was worshipped and used in white as well as black magic wherever inspiration, sagacity and ingenuity were required. In ancient Druidic law, the felling of a hazel demanded "a life for a life" - the usual penalty being a full-grown cow.*

### 121. Hazel *(Corylus avellana L.)*

This deciduous bushy shrub never exceeds 5 m in height. It branches freely, and has amazing powers of regeneratiom when cut back. The leaves are rounded, coming to a short point, with margins deeply incised with teeth, and each resulting section toothed again. (For description of genus see p. 33) The flowers, which emerge well before the leaves, are strongly differentiated: the males growing in decorative yellow catkins, the females as tiny red tassels which catch the wind-borne pollen. They develop into the well-known hazelnut or cob nut, which sits well within a leafy husk, deeply frilled at the edges, and has its nutritious kernel enclosed in a hard brown shell. Hazel is most esteemed for its fruit, and in northern Greece many variants of this species are cultivated for the nut crop. It is found self-propagated in the mixed woodlands of Thrace, Macedonia, Epirus and Thessaly, but only rarely further south.

### 122. Turkish hazel *(Corylus colurna L.)*

This medium-sized deciduous tree, which does not grow as a bush, neverthelesss much resembles *C. avellana (q. v.)* in the characteristics of its leaf, flower and fruit. (For description of genus see p. 33) The chief difference is in the husk which encloses the nut. For Turkey hazel this leafy envelope divides at its upper edges into long, narrow, hairy lobes which surround the fruit like the arms of an octopus. Turkey hazel grows

1 *Hazel*  2 *Cultivated hazel*  3 *Hazel*  4 *Turkish hazel*

as a self-propagating species in northern Greece as far south as Akarnania, where it is found in mixed deciduous woods, standing singly or in small clumps.

## Alder

*Homer's Odysey mentions the alder as forming a wood around the cave of the goddess Calypso, daughter of Atlas, and the Greek name for alder derives from the verb "to confine, to close in". Alder, besides making excellent charcoal, was long used for dyes: red from its bark, green from the flowers, brown from the twigs. The fact that when cut, alderwood, though white, seems to bleed crimson, caused it to be regarded with sacred awe. A water-loving tree, it resists corruption and its wood makes excellent conduits, or piles such as were used for the earliest European houses which were built on the edges of lakes. Finally, green alder branches are said to make the very best whistles.*

### 123. Black or Common alder *(Alnus glutinosa Gaertner)*

The spreading limbs of this medium-sized deciduous tree of at the most 20 m in height branch form a straight trunk, which in mature specimens shows irregular squares and fissures in its grey or black bark. The alternate leaves, blunt in outline with notched margins and strong veins, are vivid green at first and darken later; they seem to stick to the fingers when touched. The male catkin expands in spring into a purplish-brown collection of flowers with bright yellow pollen; the female catkin, previously only a short-stalked oval club, swells after fertilisation into what are called "false cones", which change from green and hard to woody by autumn. Having shed the tiny seeds from beneath the scales — each seed having a small float which aids dispersal by water — the empty blackened false cones remain on the tree all winter, making it easy to recognise. Black alder always grows where there is a sufficient supply of water, on the banks of rivers and streams and in ravines, but also in suitable locations in the mountains, plains and lowlands, exclusively in the northern parts of Greece. (For description of genus see p. 33)

## Hornbeams

### 124. Hornbeam *(Carpinus betulus L.)*

The mature trunk of this deciduous, medium-sized tree has wandering ribs outside the main cylinder, called "flutes"; its bark is a smooth metallic

**1,2** *Black alder*    **3, 4, 5** *Hornbeam*

grey. The erect limbs form a neatly domed crown, carrying alternate ovate leaves, heart-shaped at the base, with serrated margins, and hairy along the veins on the underside. Both male and female flowers grow in hanging catkins, the females much smaller and greener. The small, oval, amber-coloured seeds hang in several opposite pairs on a central stalk, each backed prominently by a bract consisting of 3 pointed lobes, the middle one twice the size of the other two. Hornbeam grows in highland regions among other deciduous trees, and particularly in northern Greece. (For description of genus see p. 33) Hornbeam means "very hard wood" and its timber was formerly used for ox-yokes and the cogs of water and windmills. Today, it is still the best wood for butchers' chopping blocks.

### 125. Turkey or Oriental hornbeam (*Carpinus orientalis* Miller)

The leaves of this quite large bushy tree are alternate ovals, pointed, serrated, and up to 5 cm in length; they are carried on pubescent petioles. Male and female flowers grow in separate hanging catkins. The fertile catkins develop into layer above layer of leafy, triangular and dentate scales, each concealing a small oval seed attached to its underside. *C. orientalis* is met with in the mountains of all of mainland Greece. (For description of genus see p. 33)

## Ostrya

### 126. Hop-hornbeam (*Ostrya carpinifolia* Scop.)

This small tree of up to 15 m has leaves, early summer flowers and fruit structurally not dissimilar to those of Turkey hornbeam (*q. v.*). The bark on the trunk is rough, brown, and scaly. The hanging fruit catkins are more tightly layered than in *C. orientalis,* and the oval, leafy scales with smooth margins are greenish-white at first, becoming a yellowish fawn later. The seed is not attached to the underside but fully enclosed by the bracts as if in a small bag. This quite widespread species grows on high ground, especially in the north of Greece. (For description of genus see p. 33)

1 *Turkey hornbeam*     **2, 3, 4** *Hop-hornbeam*

# Elms

### 127. Smoothed-leaved elm *(Ulmus campestris* L. or *Ulmus minor)*

Usually medium in size, this deciduous tree tends to throw up substantial suckers from the base of its straight, smooth main trunk; at full maturity, however, it may well have attained a height of 50 m. The alternate leaves are oval with a pointed tip, serrated, deep green above and pubescent on the underside. (For description of genus see p. 33) A distinctive characteristic which makes them immediately identifiable is the asymmetrically uneven leaf base. The small, reddish, tightly bell-shaped flowers with long protruding stamens open in early spring before any of the leaves have appeared, and grow in compact clusters from one bud on last year's wood. The small, hard seed lies in the centre of a flat, papery, obovate membrane, notched at the top, with many of these clustered together. Field elm prefers low altitudes, and is common throughout Greece. The bark is utilised for a variety of pharmaceutical preparations.

### 128. European white elm or Fluttering elm *(Ulmus laevis* Pallas*)*

This deciduous tree up to 30 m. tall is similar to Field elm *(q.v.),* but produces larger leaves. The little bell flowers and the seeds, essentially those of *U. campestris,* hang from long stems, however, and the membraneous notched seedwings are neatly round, fringed with fine, hair-like eyelashes. White elm likes cool forest locations among other deciduous trees or conifers. It is to be found here and there in many parts of Greece, but is a relatively rare species in this country. (For description of genus see p. 33)

### 129. Wych elm *(Ulmus montana* With.*)*

Another tree similar to Field elm *(q. v.),* this species is also occasionally as tall as 50 m but generally much smaller, with many suckers. The 5-8 cm long leaves are deep green, glossy above and downily pubescent on the underside. The flowers and seed stems are shorter than those of Field elm. The notched, membraneous seedwing has an irregularly undulating margin. Wych elm grows among other deciduous trees and conifers in the mixed highland forests of all of mainland Greece and the Peloponnese. (For description of genus see p. 33)

**1, 2, 3** *Field elm*    **4** *European white elm*    **5, 6** *Wych elm*

# Abelicea

### 130. Abelicea *(Abelicea cretica* Sm. *Zelkova Cretica* Spach.)*

This rather small deciduous tree, no taller than 10 m, is the only species of this Asiatic genus to be found in Europe. Its simple leaves, with prominent and widely spaced dentation, have 5-8 straight veins on each side of the central rib. The fertile female flowers grow singly in the leaf axils towards the ends of the twigs; the unpetalled male flowers appear as stamen clusters just below. The fruit is small, hard, and downily pubescent. *Abelicea cretica* is endemic to Crete, where it grows in rocky locations. (For description of genus see p. 33)

# Nettle Trees

### 131. Nettle tree *(Celtis australis* L.)*

This medium-sized deciduous tree grows to 25 m in height at the most. The leaves, alternate, dentate and oval, curve to a fine point and are from 6-10 cm long; they are somewhat oblique at the base and slightly pubescent, as are the flexible younger shoots. The yellowy green flowers grow singly on long stems in the leaf axils. The small, round, black and fleshy drupe hangs on a stalk 2-3 times longer than the petiole of the corresponding leaf, and has a sweet taste. A common species, nettle tree flourishes all over Greece. (For description of genus see p. 34)

### 132. Balkan nettle tree *(Celtis tournefortii* Lam.)*

This variety of *Celtis* more often grows as a large bush, but when found in tree form it is up to 6 m high. Its leaves are very similar to those of *C. australis (q. v.),* but rather smaller (2-7 cm) and completely hairless. The flowers, too, resemble those of *C. australis*. The drupe is rather more oval, orange to red, and borne on a short stalk of a about the same length as that of the corresponding leaf. This tree is common all over southern Greece. (For description of genus see p. 34)

**1** *Abelicea*    **2, 3, 4** *Nettle tree*    **5** *Balkan nettle tree*

# Oaks

*According to Robert Graves, the ancient celtic Druids were originally immigrants from the Greek peninsula, who brought their oak ("duir") worship with them. In Greece the oak was sacred to Zeus (as also to Jehovah, Allah, Thor); there was an oracular oak in the groves at Dodona, centre of the Greek oak cult, and the oracular ship Argo was made of oak timber. Mythologically the oak is much linked with lightning, the wolf totem, and royalty, and Frazer's Golden Bough has a mass of information on oak-king beliefs and practices. Oaks are extremely long-lived and can stand for over 1,000 years.*

### 133. Hungarian oak *(Quercus conferta Kit.)*

This large, deciduous tree has an imposing and densely foliated crown. It is one of the sessile oaks, whose acorn fruits are stalkless (those with fruit borne on long stalks, or peduncles, are peduncular oaks). Hungarian oak can easily be distinguished from other species of the genus (for description see p. 34) by the particularly deep indentations between the narrow segments of its relatively large (10-18 cm), obovately sphenoid leaves with rudimentary stipules. The young twigs, the leaf buds, and the underside of the leaves are all pubescent. The male flowers are small, greenish-yellow, loosely strung on long hanging stalks resembling catkins. The green female flowers nestle in the leaf axils, many of them together on a very short, thick stem. The acorn fruit is oval, its lower third enclosed by a cup made up of small, oval to lanceolate downy bracteoles, set together less tightly than in other oaks. It is green at first, ripening to brown. Hungarian oak is widespread throughout mainland Greece, but found chiefly in the north. It stands among other deciduous trees in highland and semi-highland zones.

### 134. Sessile or Durmast oak *(Quercus petraea (Mattuschka) Liebl.)*

The large crown of this tall tree is carried on a strong, straight trunk, with a fine pattern of irregular ribs in its grey bark, and capable of attaining considerable girth. The leaves, with rudimentary stipules, are medium-sized and rather varied in shape, but always pinnately lobed. Characteristic of the species is the long leaf stalk of between 1-1.5 cm, as

**1, 2, 3** *Hungarian oak*     **4, 5** *Sessile oak*

are the acorns, which grow in pairs almost without stalk in the leaf axils. (For description of genus see p. 34). The shell of the acorn cup is densely covered with oval, fuzzy, pointed bracteoles, which turn from green to brown as the fruit matures. Sessile oak grows almost anywhere in Greece in highland and semi-highland locations.

### 135. Haas oak *(Quercus pedunculiflora* C. Koch or *Quercus haas* Kotschy)

Haas oak grows up to 40 m tall and has a thick, almost perfectly round trunk. The leaves, like the flowers, are very similar to those of the two species described previously (for description of genus see p. 34); they are lightly pubescent on the underside and carried on very short petioles of about half a cm. The acorns of this sessile species ripen in pairs, and have long slim stalks which, like the cup and the young twigs, are again pubescent. *Q. pedunculiflora* is widespread among the shrubs of semi-highland zones almost anywhere in Greece.

### 136. Common or Pedunculate oak *(Quercus robur* L.)

This deciduous tree is quite representative in general of the oak family (for description of genus see p. 34), but its short-stalked leaves are somewhat smaller, more broadly sphenoid, and glabrous. The flowers are typical of the genus. The acorns grow as many as 5 together on a long, common stalk. The oval, pointed bracteoles of the cup-covering are also smooth, not pubescent. This species is met with in deciduous mountain forests or growing among shrubs at lower altitudes.

### 137. Downy or White oak *(Quercus pubescent* Willd.)

This relatively small tree is generally much contorted in its growth. Its leaves of only 5-10 cm vary greatly in shape from one plant to another. Sometimes the individual lobes are quite regular and simple as in other oaks (for description of genus see p. 34), at other times they are further subdivided in rather angular fashion into yet smaller lobes. They are tough and leathery, more often with squarish margins, and borne on very short petioles; on the underside they are covered in thick fuzz, as the

**1** *Haas oak*    **2, 3, 4** *Common oak*    **5, 6** *Downy oak*

name implies. In fact, even the flower petals have hairy tufts at the tips. Pubescent oak sheds its leaves late, not until the middle or even the end of winter. The acorns are rather slender ovals; the greyish-green, pointed cup-bracteoles are again highly pubescent. This species is found on the lower mountain slopes throughout Greece.

### 138. Bitter or Turkey oak *(Quercus cerris* L.*)*

At first sight this tree, growing to 40 m in height, looks like Pedunculate oak *(q.v.),* but a closer look will differentiate it by the deep bark fissures showing a bzight tangerine-orange colour. The leaves are soft, pubescent on the underside, and relatively long and narrow with curious, asymmetrically stepped lobes. The petioles are short. The winter buds end in tassels of long brown hairs. The female flowers grow either singly or in groups of up to four on short, thick and hairy stems; the four very long, pointed and curving petals are finely ciliated. The male catkins are semi-erect. The acorn of this species is shallow and squat, half of it submerged in the cup, the bracteoles of which each have an odd, leafy outgrowth, creating an overall mossy appearance. Bitter oak flourishes almost anywhere in Greece at high and medium altitudes. (For description of genus see p. 34)

### 139. Valonea oak *(Quercus aegilops* L. or *macrolepis* Korschy*)*

This is a species which sheds its leaves late in winter, and is noticeable for the disproportionly large girth of its trunk. (For description of genus see p. 34) The leaves, on the other hand, are relatively small, tough and pubescent, and carried on medium-sized petioles. They are pointed ovals rather than the sphenoid shape typical of oak, with their margins deeply cut into curved points not quite large enough to qualify as separate lobes. The large acorns are short and squat, like those of Bitter oak *(q.v.),* and to a good half of their depth covered by the cup. The cup-scales are long, tongue-shaped ovals more or less curving back on themselves, giving the fruit an if anything even more wrapped-up look than do the mossy cups of Bitter oak. Q. aegilops flourishes all over Greece, at sea level and on high ground.

**1** *Downy oak*    **2, 3** *Bitter oak*    **4** *Valonea oak*

1

2

3

4

## 140. Euboean oak *(Quercus euboica* Papaioannou*)*

This tree now grows as a rather large bush up to 3 m in height. It appears, however, that in the past it developed as a tree in the same locations where it is to be found today, forming whole groves of large trees which fell victim to fire or the axe. The leaves of Euboean oak (for description of genus see p. 34) resemble those of Valonea oak *(q.v.)* more than other species; they have shorter petioles, however, and are even longer and narrower, with large pointed serrations in the margins. They are dark green above and lighter green on the underside. The typical oak flowers produce oval acorns up to 2 cm long, as many as 6 of them growing from a medium-sized common stalk. The bracteoles covering the cup are hairy, and those nearer the rim curve outwards slightly. The species is endemic to north-eastern Euboea.

## 141. Lusitania oak *(Quercus lusitanica* Lam. *Q. infectoria* Oliv.*)*

This relatively small tree was known even in ancient times for its oak-apples. These are small, woody balls which appear among the leaves through the intervention of the insect *Cynips tinctoria* - Kynips the dyer - whose product, the oak-apples, were valued for their use in medicinal preparations and for tanning and dying. Oak-apples are not, of course, exclusive to *Q. lusitanica,* but on this species they are found in greater quantity and better quality. The 4-8 cm long leaves of Lusitanian oak are simple, slim, barely pointed ovals, tough-skinned, deep green above and light green on the underside, and with dentate margins. They remain on the tree until almost the end of the winter, falling only just before the new leaves appear. As a result, the tree is classed as a semi-evergreen. The flowers and acorns resemble those of Sessile oak *(q.v.).* Lusitanian oak, a rare species in Greece, grows in Thrace and on the island of Lesbos, either singly or in small groves. (For description of genus see p. 34)

## 142. Macedonian oak *(Quercus trojana* Webb or *Quercus macedonica* (Alph.) D.C.*)*

Another semi-evergreen oak, this species also retains its leaves until just before the new ones emerge. The straight, tapering trunk rarely exceeds 15 m in height, and the branches spread horizontally. The 4-8 cm long leaves are blunt ovals with widely-spaced serrations, a deep

**1, 2** *Valonea oak*      **3** *Euboean oak*      **4** *Lusitanian oak*      **5** *Macedonian oak*

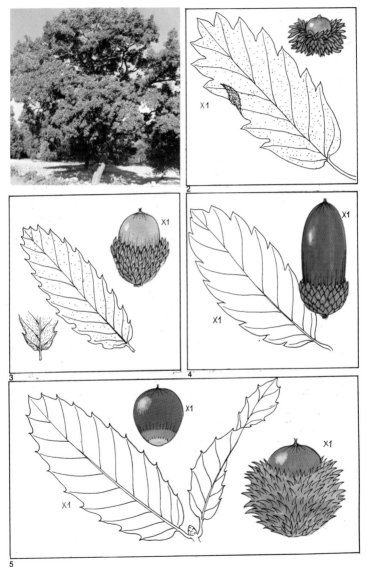

green above and lighter green on the underside. The flower structure is typical for both sexes (for description of genus see p. 34), the almost stemless females growing 2-3 together. The unusual feature of this species is the acorn, which is relatively small, has a curiously recessed tip, and is almost totally submerged in the cup. The lower bracteoles are tightly stuck to the bottom of the cup, those nearer the rim curl outwards. As the name implies, this species is found in Macedonia, Thrace and Thessaly, in woodlands at high and intermediate altitudes. A subspecies is known to exist in Arcady.

### 143. Lucombe oak *(Quercus hispanica* Lam.*)*

This species appears to be a natural hybrid of Bitter oak *(Q. cerris) (q. v.)* and the Mediterranean cork-oak *(Q. suber)* of the Iberian peninsula and presents characteristics of both. Lucombe oak bark is of far lower quality, however, than that of the real cork tree (which, incidentally, withstands the periodical removal of its outer bark, a process which will kill any other tree). *Q. hispanica* is of medium size, with hard, pointed leaves, oval or elliptical, with coarsely but regular dentate margins, green above and greyish-white on the underside. The oval acorns are set one-third of their length in ash grey, hairy cups, the pointed bracteoles of which curl outwards. The leaves stay on the tree until just before the winter's end. Lucombe oak prefers dry soils rich in lime, growing in the Pindus mountains, in Arcady, on Rhodes, and elsewhere in Greece. (For description of genus see p. 34)

### 144. Holm oak *(Quercus ilex* L.*)*

This properly evergreen native of the Mediterranean is also a species of oak (for description of genus see p. 34) although it looks much more like a giant holly. It usually grows as a shrub, but more mature specimens can evolve into quite large trees. There are many holm oaks in the National Garden in Athens, planted at the time of Queen Amalia, which have now attained heights of 15 m or so. The lanceolate leaves have slightly inrolled edges, are dark green above and grey-green on the underside, but vary greatly in size and even shape, sometimes being whole,

1 *Lucomb oak*    2, 3, 4 *Holm oak*

sometimes serrated. They always have a thick leathery texture to prevent moisture loss, Each leaf lives for about three years before it turns brown and falls. The flowers follow the normal oak pattern. The short-stalked acorns are tapered ovals, set in quite small cups with ordinary, evenly layered bracteoles. The bark is used for tanning, and the wood gives a very high quality charcoal. Holm oak flourishes in particularly hot and dry locations, and will grow almost anywhere in Greece on dry slopes with limey soils.

### 145. Kerm oak or Holly oak *(Quercus coccifera L.)*

*The kerm oak is the tree from which the ancients obtained their scarlet dye. It was sacred to the gods Mars and Negal.*

Kerm oak is common in Greece as a more or less large shrub, but in those parts of the country where there are fewer goats to graze on the tender young shoots it is capable of becoming a large tree which can live for many hundreds of years. Though kerm oak belongs to the genus *quercus* (for description see p. 34), its hard, shiny and spiny leaves closely resemble those of holly and stay on the tree all through the year. The typical oak-genus flowers produce oval acorns in cups layered with hard, pointed bracteoles curving outwards. It is a common species on dry, stony slopes at low altitudes throughout Greece.

## Sweet Chestnut

### 146. Sweet chestnut *(Castanea sativa Miller)*

This very large deciduous tree carries a densely foliated domed crown on a trunk of considerable girth. The leaves, on short petioles, are 10-25 cm long, lanceolate, with serrated margins. The small male flowers grow strung on erect catkins almost as long as the leaves, several of them together and pointing in different directions like a cream-coloured star. The female flowers, encased within a prickly cupule, nestle usually in threes in the leaf axils further down. After fertilisation the cupule expands and eventually forms the case around the fruit, the edible chestnut. Sweet chestnut, never found in lowland plains, always grows at moderate altitudes among other deciduous trees, where it is very common from Macedonia to Crete. Its timber is valued for furniture-making, and even its

**1, 2, 3** *Kerm oak*  **4** *Sweet chestnut*  **5** *Sweet chestnut, male flowers*  **6** *Sweet chestnut, and female flower*

2

3

4

5

6

155

decomposed wood and the sawdust are much in demand by gardeners as they make an excellent humus. (For description of genus see p. 31)

# Beeches

### 147. European beech *(Fagus silvatica* L.*)*

This is a large deciduous tree, easily known by the metallic grey of its smooth bark. It grows up to 35 m tall, with a straight trunk and branches inclining upwards; the younger twigs are rather zig-zag, with long, pointed, alternate buds. The leaves measure 4-10 cm in length, and have wavy margins, short cilia, and short petioles. The male flower is a small, hairy, four-lobed greenish calyx with about 8 yellow stamens; 15 or so of these form a round, bobble-like catkin hanging from a long stalk with 2 small stipules. The very small, almost stalkless female flowers grow two each within an oval green cupule. During the summer the cupules expand, become hard and woody, and develop soft brown spines as well as a stalk as long as the cupule. When mature, they split at the top and reveal 1-2 beechnuts within. These are triangular in shape, with a hard, smooth brown shell and a white kernel. *Fagus silvatica* is common on high ground in the north, where it forms extensive groves. The furthest south it is found on Mt Oxya in Roumeli. Since in Greece this tree seldom stands alone, it is less broad than European specimens, and its branches point upwards more towards the light. (For description of genus see p. 34)

### 148. Oriental beech *(Fagus orientalis* Lipsky*)*

This species superficially resembles *F. silvatica (q. v.)*, but has larger leaves (5-15 cm), broader at the tip, and provided with stipules. It also differs with regard to its flowers and fruits, both of which have longer stalks, in the mature seed twice the length of the cupule. Oriental beech is found in forest locations among other deciduous trees, or in extensive homogeneous groves in north-eastern Greece, particularly in Macedonia and Thrace. (For description of genus see p. 34)

### 149. Turkey beech *(Fagus moesiaca* (Maly, Domin) Czeez*)*

Turkey beech is again very similar to European beech *(q. v.)*, the only difference being details of the male and female flowers and the fruit. It grows in mixed deciduous woods, often alongside other species of beech

**1, 2** *European beech*     **3** *Oriental beech*     **4** *Turkey beech*

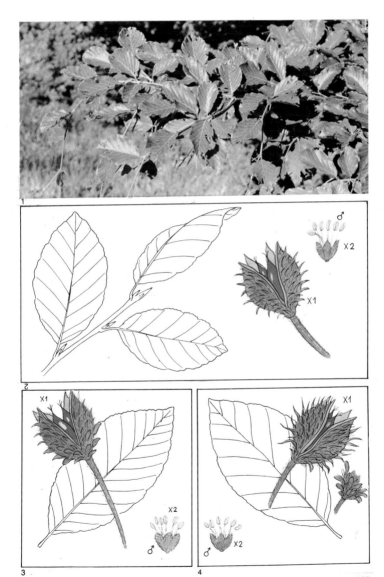

in the highlands of northern and central Greece. (For description of genus see p. 34). Turkey beech is believed to be a natural hybrid of *F.silvatica* and *F. orientalis* described above.

# Christ-Thorn

**150. Christ-thorn** or **Jerusalem thorn** *(Paliurus aculeatus* Lam. or *Paliurus spina-christi,* Miller*)*

This is a deciduous shrub of 2-3 m in height. It has flexible zig-zag branches with many spines, either straight or recurved. The 2-4 cm long leaves are oval, triple-veined, and finely dentate, and have two sharp spines at the base of the petiole. The tiny yellow flowers grow in small axillary clusters. The flattened disc-shaped fruit has a large membraneous round wingblade with a wavy margin. Christ-thorn is common everywhere in scrubland at medium and low altitudes. (For description of genus see p. 34)

# Walnut

**151. European** or **Common walnut** *(Juglans regia* L.*)*

This deciduous tree up to 25 m tall has a broad domed crown on a trunk of thick grey ribs with shiny faces. The pinnately compound leaves have 7 smooth elliptical folioles each, and give off a characteristic aroma. The juice of leaves and fruit stains a persistent suntan brown. The male flowers grow in hanging caterpillar-like catkins; the very small, flask-shaped female flowers stand upright in twos and threes. Both types are green and appear in the leaf axils. The short-stalked fruit is the familiar walnut, which at first is covered in a green fleshy case. It may already be eaten at this stage or, complete with case, pickled in vinegar. If left to ripen fully, the green case drops away and the nut, now with a hard, wrinkled woody shell enclosing the actual kernel, is exposed. *Juglans regia* is found throughout Greece among other woodland trees in the highland belt. It is much cultivated everywhere in the country for its oily, highly nutritious nut. (For description of genus see p. 34)

**1, 2** *Christ-thorn*     **3, 4, 5** *European walnut*

# Poplars

## 152. White poplar *(Populus alba L.)*

*This was the tree which Hercules, who conquered death, was sent to fetch from the springs of the Ister, and it is mentioned in the Odyssey and Aeneid as another of the three trees of resurrection growing around the cave of Calypso (alder and cypress are the other two). Hesiod reports that the valley of the Styx is full of white poplars. In later ages, poplar leaves became an indispensable ingredient in the recipe for the ointment which made European witches able to fly to their "wicked rendezvous".*

This large deciduous tree has rather upright branches borne on straight trunks of smooth, greenish-white bark which in maturity turns black and develops rhomboid fissures. The shape of the leaves varies greatly, even on the same tree, from simple and almost round with dentate or wavy margins, to palmately compound with 5 lobes. The underside is white and thickly downy, the upper a rich, dark green, turning to bright gold in the autumn. As in all poplars (a name derived from the ancient Greek word for "to flutter" — c.p. also French *papillon* for butterfly), they are set on long, flexible petioles with an odd twist so that they move in the slightest breeze. (For description of genus see p. 34) On the male trees, the catkins appear before the leaves; each bract has crimson stamens with golden anthers. On the female trees the catkins are strung much more loosely; they ripen into greenish-brown woody capsules containing numerous seeds, each with a tuft of white hairs, which drift away on the wind like snowflakes. White poplar grows in damp locations all over Greece in lowlands and the lower highlands, near rivers or lakes and, since it resists salty sea winds, also near the coast.

## 153. Aspen *(Populus tremula L.)*

*Golden head-dresses of aspen leaves have been found in Mesopotamian burials of 3,000 B.C.*

The trunk of this medium-sized poplar (for description of genus see p. 34) has smooth grey bark with characteristic diamond-shaped hollows, and a broad crown. Its leaves are almost round, only slightly

**1, 2** *White poplar*   **3, 4** *Aspen*

pointed at the tip, with wavy margins; they are somewhat darker green on the upper side and shiny on both surfaces. The long slim petiole is flattened sideways, so that the leaf trembles in the very lightest breath of air. The flower pattern is that of White poplar *(q. v.)*. Aspen too is a thirsty tree, sustaining much moisture loss through the constant movement of its leaves, and grows in damp woodlands on high ground in northern and central Greece.

### 154. Black poplar *(Populus nigra L.)*

*In pre-Hellenic Greece, Black poplar had different divinitory uses from White poplar* (q. v.), *and was the funereal tree sacred to Mother Earth.*

The thick, straight trunk of this large deciduous and much-branched tree has pale grey bark, irregularly ribbed. The leaves, set on the typical twisting petioles (for description of genus see p. 34) are pointed ovals or triangles. The flower pattern is that of White poplar *(q. v.)*. **Populus nigra** frequents river banks and damp locations generally at medium and low altitudes. Lately it has been much cultivated for its timber, which proves lighter, tougher, and more flexible than other woods. *P. nigra italica,* or **Lombardy poplar,** is the familiar, very tall and narrow-crowned variety often planted as windbreaks; the large majority of the trees are male.

# Willows

*The willow, or osier, was sacred in Greece to Hecate, Circe, Hera and Persephone, all of them aspects of the Triple Moon-goddess who also ruled the tides. Their remote common predecessor Belili, sister of Tammuz, was already the goddess of willows and of wells and springs. By extension, Apollo is shown as receiving the gift of musical inspiration by touching willow trees in a grove of Persephone's, as shown in Polygnotos' famous picture at Delphi. In later times, willow trees were much worshipped by witches, whose name—like 'wicker', and 'wicked' too — derives from "willow". It was willow baskets that were the sieves in which they confessed going to sea in the time of King James I and VI.*

### 155. White willow *(Salix alba L.)*

This rather large deciduous tree of up to 25 m in height has a short, fat trunk with grey bark, often twisted or divided or both. The supple, brownish-yellow twigs are pubescent. The leaves are spear-shaped,

**1, 2, 3** *Black poplar*    **4** *White willow, male flowers*    **5** *White willow, female flowers*

narrow, and at first covered with white down on both surfaces, later only on the underside. The resultant colour effect has given the tree its name. Both the male and female flower catkins are borne semi-erect on the same tree, the females ripening into a large number of tiny seeds, each with a tuft of white hairs. White willow grows on the banks of streams and rivers almost anywhere throughout Greece. It yields salicine, medicinally used as a substitute for quinine. (For description of genus *see p. 35)*

### 156. French willow *(Salix amygdalina* L. or *Salix triandra)*

This willow grows as a bush or as a small tree of up to 5 m, with a much divided, rather tasselled crown. The leaves are lanceolate, resembling almond leaves. The flower pattern follows that of *S. alba* and, like that species, this willow too is commonly found on river banks, by lakesides, and growing in damp ravines. (For description of genus *see p. 35)*

### 157. Goat willow or Great sallow *(Salix caprea* L.)

The name of this species, which grows as a bush or a small tree of up to 10 m, comes from the particular attraction its spring shoots have for goats. It has somewhat more spreading branches than other willows. Its large leaves, 5-15 cm, are fat ovals curving to a point and with prominent veins. Both the male and the female flowers are contained in the much-loved "willow-pussies", oval structures clad in a thick mass of soft, silky, white hairs. They appear before the leaves. The male flowers have two long stamens with golden anthers. The tiny ripe seeds are hair-tufted and dispersed by the wind. Goat willow flourishes in damp locations, usually along streams in mountain forests. It can be found throughout mainland Greece. (For description of genus *see p. 35)*

### 158. Grey willow or Grey sallow *(Salix cinerea* L.)

This bushy willow attains 6 m in height at the most. Its young shoots are liberally covered with an ashy-grey down. The leaves are obovate or sphenoid, narrower at the base; a greyish pubescence covers the upper

**1** *White willow*   **2, 3, 4** *French willow*   **5** *Goat willow*

surface, and the underside is a paler, whitish grey. The erect catkins appear before the leaves. Grey willow can be found in damp locations nearly all over Greece. (For description of genus see p. 35)

### 159. Grey-barked or Horry willow *(Salix incana* Scop.)

This too is a willow of frequently bushy growth, or may become a small tree of up to 8 m tall, densely branched. The flower pattern is typical for the genus (for description see p. 35). The leaves of this species, very slim and long, rather look like ribbons; they are green above and white, with dense pubescence, on the underside. *S. incana* grows in highland ravines in almost all the Greek mountains.

### 160. Crack willow *(Salix fragilis* L.)

This 5-15 m high tree with broadly spreading limbs has the remarkable characteristic that its branches break off very easily and do so with an audible "crack!". Such torn-off twigs, carried downstream, strike root where they get stranded on damp banks. The lanceolate leaves of this species are very pointed; at first they are pubescent, later completely smooth on both surfaces. The flowers (for description of genus see p. 35) are borne in 3-7 cm long, drooping catkins. Crack willow grows by streams and river and on lakesides throughout Greece.

### 161. Sweet or Bay willow *(Salix pentandra* L.)

This large deciduous shrub or tree has broad spear-shaped leaves, a glossy dark green above and dull on the underside, somewhat resembling bay-leaves. When young they are sticky and aromatic. The catkins are borne stiffly upright, each flower having 5 conspicuous stamens. (For description of genus see p. 35) Sweet willow likes damp locations by rivers and lakes, and can be found all over Greece.

**1** *Grey willow*   **2, 3** *Grey-barked willow*   **4, 5** *Crack willow*   **6** *Sweet willow*

### 162. **Purple osier** (Salix purpurea L.)

Mostly this species grows as a bush, sometimes it is a small tree 1-5 m in height. The bark of its branches is a reddish purple, becoming rather more grey in maturity. The leaves are very slim, tapering oblongs, borne in opposite pairs on very long petioles. The short catkins of 2-4 cm are erect, and the flower stamens purple. (For description of genus see p. 35) Purple willow, due to its flexible branches, is one of the osiers (see Basket willow). It frequents river banks pretty well all over Greece.

### 163. **Basket willow** or **Common osier** (Salix viminalis L.)

*This willow, like Purple osier above, belongs to the frequently cultivated osier willows with exceptionally supple stems used for basket-making. In Europe, osiers for this work are grown from cuttings in swampy, so-called osier-beds. The first year's growth is cut back, forming a "stool" which will send up many new shoots every spring. These grow to 2 m long and are harvested every year, to be used either with the bark intact or stripped.*

This generally bushy species may at times become a small tree, though never larger than 4 m in height; it has extremely flexible, pubescent branches. The slender, ribbon-like leaves are 10-20 cm long and pointed, smooth above and silvery pubescent on the underside. The small "willow pussies" develop from flowers as described for Goat willow (q. v.). Basket willow is commonly found along riverbanks in northern Greece. (For description of genus see p. 35)

### 164. **Eared sallow** (Salix aurita L.)

This species of willow, rare in Greece, grows as a bush of about 1-3 m in height and has spreading branches. Its leaves, which are responsible for its name, are obovate and rather curly, with a twisted, pointed tip. The flowers appear in short, erect catkins with noticeable stipules. (For description of genus see p. 35) The only location where this species has been observed in Greece is in some marshes in Macedonia.

## Box

### 165. **Box** (Buxus sempervirens L.)

This evergreen shrub is only very rarely found growing as a small tree, when it is at the most up to 8 m tall. The small elliptical or obovate leaves,

**1** *Purple osier*    **2** *Basket willow*    **3** *Eared sallow*    **4, 5** *Box*

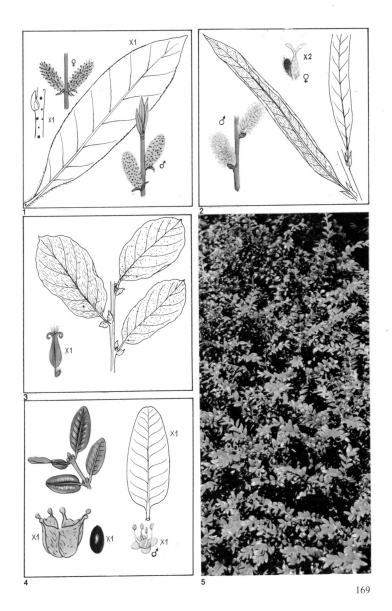

shiny and leathery, grow in opposite pairs; they give off a very strong, characteristic smell. The very small yellowish-green flowers are borne in dense, stalkless clusters. The hard drupes are brown and divided into three sections. Box grows at high altitudes, both in forests and in the *maquis*. It can be found almost anywhere in mainland Greece, on Rhodes, Mytilene and Siros, but not in the Peloponnese. (For description of genus see p. 35)

# Rhododendrons

### 166. Yellow rhododendron *(Rhododendron luteum Sweet)*

This low evergreen shrub grows from 50 cm to 2 m in height. Its branches are pubescent, bearing 5-20 cm long oblong leaves, sphenoid at the base; the young leaves are also pubescent, but become smooth later. The leaf margins are whole. The strikingly beautiful, apricot-yellow flowers are 5-7 cm in diameter, with 5 lobes spreading out at the top of a cone-shaped corolla tube. The fruit is a round, brown, hard capsule. This species originated in western Asia, and can be found in Greece only in one area on the island of Mytilene (Lesbos). (For description of genus see p. 35)

### 167. Rhododendron *(Rhododendron ponticum L.)*

This is a large, evergreen shrub of up to 3 m, with pointed oblong leaves 7-12 cm long. They are glossy above and a dull, lighter green on the underside. The flower, 4-5 cm in diameter, is a strong cyclamen-pink, with slightly darker stigmata towards the centre. The wide funnel of the corolla has 5 spreading petal-lobes, longer than the tube. The flowers grow in tight bunches on long stems from the branch terminals. The fruit is a brown, woody capsule. *R. ponticum* can be found self-propagated in the forests of Thrace. (For description of the genus see p. 35)

# Arbutus

### 168. Strawberry-tree *(Arbutus unedo L.)*

This is an evergreen shrub with rough bark, rarely taller than 1-3 m. Its oblong, serrated leaves are smooth and dark green above, lighter green on the underside. The small white, or occasionally pink, flower is flask-shaped, with the calyx divided by tiny serrations at the mouth into minute

**1, 2** *Yellow rhododendron*   **3** *Rhododendron*   **4** *Strawberry-tree*

lobes. It is **borne** terminally on reddish, branched stalks in drooping, multi-flowered clusters. The fruit is a round, warty berry, with a slight resemblance to strawberry, 1.5-2 cm across, red or orange in colour. Its sweet, mealy flesh is edible, and also used for liqueurs and preserves. Strawberry-tree is common throughout Greece in low-altitude scrubland. (For description of genus see p. 35)

**169. Greek strawberry-tree** *(Arbutus andrachne* L.*)*

This rather larger evergreen shrub-species reaches up to 4 m in height, and has a remarkably smooth, red bark. The leaves are grey-green, oblong, with smooth margins. The flowers are similar to those of *A. unedo* above *(q. v.)*, but are carried in erect clusters. (For description of genus see p. 35) The fruit is small, only 6 mm in diameter, hard, and ripens from yellow to orange to red. *A. andrachne* grows throughout Greece in scrubland at medium and low altitudes.

# Heathers

**170. Tree-heath** *(Erica arborea* L.*)*

This 1-5 m high evergreen shrub has erect branches densely covered with successive whorls of 3 or 4 very small, linear, bright green leaves. The flowers appear in early spring, white or dull pink, shaped like tiny bells with slightly protruding crimson anthers. They grow pyramidally massed up to the very tips of the straight branches. Tree-heath grows in the *maquis* at lower altitudes, and is common in many regions, especially in the south of the country. (For description of genus see p. 35)

There are other species of heather in Greece, the low growth of which does not allow their classification as shrubs. One of these is **Verticillate heather** *(E. verticiliata)*, up to 8 cm, the pink flowers of which appear in the autumn, and which grows in scrubland like *E. arborea*. Another is **Snow heather** *(E. carnea)* a plant which is only to be found at very high altitudes in the mountains of northern Greece; its branches spread horizontally across the rocks, and its pink flowers are few but relatively large.

Here a small shrubby plant should also be mentioned which is botanically related to both the heathers and the strawberry-trees:

**1** *Strawberry-tree*     **2, 3** *Greek strawberry-tree*     **4** *Tree-heath*

**Bilberry** *(Vaccinium myrtilius),* which grows no higher than 60 cm. Its quite tough little leaves are roundly elliptical, the flowers greenish-white or greenish-purple and bell-shaped. The drupe is a purple-black berry about the size of a pea with a sharp-edged dimple at the lower end, very juicy and sweet. Its American name is Blueberry.

# Date-Plum

### 171. Date-plum *(Diospyrus lotus* L.*)*

This small tree, sometimes found growing as a bush, is at the most 12 m high and carries a spherical crown of foliage. The leaves are elliptical or oblong, 7-14 cm long, shiny dark green above and more or less pubescent on the underside. The reddish-pink flower is flask-shaped and appears in clusters in the leaf axils. The inedible fruits are about the size of cherries, at first pale brown, later black. Date-plum grows in Macedonia and Thrace, and has also been found in the prefecture of Fthiotis in central Greece. (For description of genus see p. 36).

# Storax

### 172. Storax *(Styrax officinalis* L.*)*

This large, much-branching deciduous shrub attains heights of 2-7 m The leaves on short petioles are bluntly pointed ovals, green above, and whitish-green and thickly pubescent on the underside. The twigs and flower stems are also woolly-haired. The fragile white flowers, about 3 cm in diameter, grow in sprays of 3-6 from a common stalk, set towards the ends of the branches. Some of the petals bend back far enough to reveal long, pale-yellow anthers. The fruit is a round and fleshy drupe, its base set well inside the woolly calyx. Storax can be found in many areas of Greece, from Thrace to the Dodecanese and Crete. It prefers to grow in ravines or in forests of pine where it is protected from the summer drought. It yields a resinous vanilla-scented balsam formerly much used in medicine and perfumery. Its sweet exhalation is mentioned in Ecclesiasticus XXIV.15 as an attribute of wisdom. (For description of genus see p. 36).

**1, 2** *Date-plum*     **3, 4, 5** *Storax*

175

# Oleander

### 173. Oleander or Roseberry spurge *(Nerium oleander L.)*

This evergreen shrub, 1-5 m high, is a familiar sight to visitors to Greece as it is much planted along the road and highways. It is less well known that its sap is poisonous, earning it a secondary name of Bitter laurel. The branches shoot straight out of the ground; they are erect and covered all the way up with pointed, lanceolate leaves of about 15 cm length with a marked central rib. The large, scented, usually rose-coloured flowers of up to 5 cm across are borne in luxurious, multi-stemmed clusters at the branch terminals. The corolla spreads into 5 blunt petals, with additional short-toothed lobes at the throat. The flowers continue to bloom all through the summer. The brown, woody fruit-pod is long, narrow and elegantly striped, and splits in two lengthways when it is ripe; the sections curl back and across each other to release the small seeds, each provided with a large silky tassel of hair to aid wind dispersal. Self-propagated, Oleander is common throughout Greece, growing at lower altitudes by rivers and at the bottoms of mountain ravines. There are also varieties with white, creamy-yellow, or crimson flowers. (For description of genus see p. 36)

# Olive

### 174. Olive tree *(Olea europaea L. s.sp. oleander)*

The olive is a medium-sized evergreen tree, occasionally growing as a shrub, rarely taller than 10 m, but capable of attaining a very great age. Its grey trunk is often gnarled and twisted. The small, opposite, grey-green leaves on very short petioles are spear-shaped or oblong, and silvery on the underside. The very small cruciform creamy flowers grow in short, dense, erect and elongated axillary clusters. The fruit is a purple-black, shiny drupe with a long, rather narrowly oval seed stone. Wild olive is met with in low-altitude scrubland throughout Greece. In its cultivated form it

**1, 2** *Oleander*      **3** *Olive tree*

1

2

3

grows in scores of varieties all over the country wherever the climate is mild. (For description of genus see p. 36)

*Greek mythology has it that Hercules' club was made from the wood of wild olive, as well it might have been, since olive wood is exceptionally hard and durable.*

# Privet

### 175. Common privet or Primwort *(Ligustrum vulgare* L.*)*

This deciduous species grows either as a bush or as a small tree up to 5 m in height. The smooth, thick leaves are elliptical, rounded at the tip, and set in opposite pairs. The flowers (for description of genus see p. 36) grow in slim spikes at the branch terminals; they have a strong, sweet scent. The small black drupe has oily flesh and contains from 2-4 seeds. Common privet grows widely in scrubland at medium and low altitudes almost all over Greece.

# Lilac

### 176. Common lilac *(Syringa vulgaris* L.*)*

The leaves of this deciduous shrub of 1-6 m height are oval and pointed. The small, pale purple flowers are massed in dense, pyramidal clusters towards the branch terminals. (For description of genus see p. 37) The seed is a very small oval capsule with a yellowish, leathery skin. Lilac grows in stony regions of northern Greece as far up as Thessaly. It is much cultivated for the strong, beautiful scent of its flowers.

**1, 2** *Olive tree*     **3, 4** *Common privet*     **5** *Common lilac*

179

# Mock Privets

### 177. Mock privet *(Phillyrea latifolia L.)*

This large, evergreen shrub grows up to 8 m tall, with robust, spreading branches. (For description of genus see p. 36) The very small, greeenish-yellow flowers, in structure like those of *Ligustrum vulgare (q. v.)*, grow in rounded axillary clusters about 1 cm across in the leaf axils. The fruits are small, fleshy, round drupes, blue-black with an eye at the tip. Mock privet is common in the *maquis* at medium and low altitudes pretty well all over Greece.

### 178. Small mock privet *(Phillyrea media L.)*

This smaller species only grows up to 5 m, with stiffly erect grey branches. The leaves and flowers again resemble those of *Ligustrum vulgare (q. v.)*, but the latter are borne in somewhat drooping clusters. (For description of genus see p. 36) The round, blue-black drupes do not have an eye at the tip like those of *P. latifolia*. This species grows in scrubland on the lower mountain slopes almost anywhere in Greece, alongside with other shrubs.

# Ash

*In Greece the ash was sacred to Poseidon. Elsewhere in mythology, the meliai or ash-spirits, which Hesiod says sprang from the blood of Uranus when Cronos castrated him, were much revered. Since the roots of the ash strangle those of other forest trees nearby, ash was regarded as the tree of power (also in Nordic mythology), and especially—via Poseidon — of sea power or power inherent in sea water.*

### 179. Flowering ash or Manna *(Fraxinus ornus L.)*

This deciduous tree rarely reaches heights exceeding 10 m. The leaves are pinnately compound with up to 10-15 elliptical or obovate folioles; they are a coppery green when they first open, later become a normal light green, and in autumn turn a rusty-red brown. Appearing

**1, 2, 3** *Mock privet*     **4** *Small mock privet*     **5, 6** *Flowering ash*

together with the leaves, very small white and sweetly scented flowers are borne in erect catkin-like structures, several of these spreading out conspicuously from the same branch terminal. They differ from the two species of ash below in having petals, and are insect-pollinated. The singly-borne seeds are small and hard, each attached to a slim, membraneous seedwing called a key. (For description of genus see p. 37) The tree yields a mildly laxative sap called "manna", and is specifically grown for this in Sicily. In Greece, ash grows almost anywhere at medium altitudes in mixed forests or scrubland.

### 180. Common ash *(Fraxinus excelsior L.)*

This member of the ash family (for description of genus see p. 37) reaches up to 30 m in height. It is easily recognisable all the year round by its short black leaf-buds set in pairs; the trunk has typical ash-grey bark, in mature specimens developing a symmetrical pattern of fissures resembling a fishing net. Leaves and flowers are like those of *F. ornus* above, but the flowers are without petals and depend on wind pollination, and the folioles have no individual petioles. The seeds are typical of the genus. Common ash grows in forests and scrubland at high altitudes in mainland Greece. In earlier times, ash wood provided sure-thrusting spears for warriors and hunters.

### 181. Caucasian ash *(Fraxinus oxycarpa* Willd, or *Fraxinus angustifolia* s.sp *oxycarpa)*

This species much resembles *F. ornus* and *F. excelsior* above *(q. v.)*, but its height is between the two: 10-20 m. The leaf and flower pattern is that of *F. excelsior.* The seedwing is rather narrow and narrows still further towards the base. (For description of genus see p. 37) As its name implies, Caucasian ash grows in damp locations in many forests all over Greece.

## Chaste Tree

### 182. Chaste Tree *(Vitex agnus-castus L.)*

This graceful deciduous shrub grows up to 3 m tall. Greek country lore considers it sinful not to crush a leaf or two to enjoy the aromatic scent it gives off. The leaves are palmately compound, and the small

**1, 2** *Common ash*     **3, 4** *Caucasian ash*     **5, 6** *Chaste-tree*

usually mauve, but sometimes pink, white, or skyblue, flowers are clustered in long spikes at the branch terminals. (For description of genus see p. 37) The small drupe is fleshy and reddish-black. Chaste tree is very common all over Greece, growing freely in ravines, on seashores, and generally where there is sufficient moisture. The name derives from its use in ancient times as a medicine to ensure chastity.

# Tea Trees

### 183. European tea-tree *(Lycium europaeum* L.)*

This deciduous shrub, 1-3 m in height, has erect branches with a liberal supply of spines. The grey-green, 2 cm leaves are simple lanceolate or spatulate with small petioles. The white or pink flowers appear on short stalks 1-3 together in the leaf axils. The round fruits are fleshy red or orange drupes. This species grows at low altitudes in many parts of Greece. (For description of genus see p. 37)

### 184. African tea-tree *(Lycium afrum* L.)*

Slightly smaller, only up to 2 m tall, this shrub has equally erect, exceedingly spiny branches. The leaves are narrowly linear and somewhat fleshy. The flowers, similar to those of *L.europaeum (q. v.)*, are mauve or blue. (For description of genus see p. 37) The round, fleshy drupe is a reddish black. *L. afrum* is found in rocky areas on Crete.

### 185. Persian tea-tree *(Lycium persicum* Miers*)*

The branches of this 1-3 m high shrub are as prickly as those of its relatives described above (for description of genus see p. 37), but in addition covered in downy pubescence. The leaves, usually also hairy, are narrowly spatulate. The blue or mauve flowers, much like those of *L. europaeum, (q. v.)*, develop into black drupes. Persian tea-tree grows in rocky soils on Crete.

### 186. Box thorn or Duke of Argyll's teaplant *(Lycium halimifolium Miller* L. or *Lycium barbarum)*

The branches of this less hostile shrub (1-3 m) are long and slim and almost spineless, and droop down towards the ground. The lanceolate leaves are greyish-green, and the pinkish-mauve axillary flowers typical of the genus (for description see p. 37). The drupe is red. This species frequents the scrubland of southern Greece, and is found especially on Crete.

1 *Chaste-tree*    2 *European tea-tree*    3 *African tea-tree*    4 *Persian tea-tree*
5 *Box thorn*

# Elders

*In folklore the elder is the tree of doom and much associated with black magic. Country babies laid in an elderwood cradle were expected to pine away (birch was the proper wood to use), and the elder has long been believed to have been the crucifixion tree. Elderleaf-shaped funerary flints found in megalithic longbarrows suggest that the tree had even then long been associated with death. Even its scent was believed to be poisonous, but its bark and flowers were used in country remedies for fevers, burns and scalds — presumably to drive out an excess of life.*

### 187. Black elder *(Sambucus nigra L.)*

This deciduous shrub or small tree grows up to 10 m in height. The leaves are pinnately compound, with 2-3 pairs of oval, pointed leaflets, the additional, terminal one on the central petiole-rib being larger than the others. (For description of genus see p. 37) The small, creamy-white, 5-petalled flowers grow in large umbels of 10-20 cm across at the branch terminals, each umbel having 5 main branches. The fruit is a small, round, fleshy blue-black drupe. Black elder grows near water, and the plant is utilised as natural hedge-fencing by the country people. Black elder is very common throughout Greece.

### 188. Red-berried or alpine elder *(Sambucus racemosa L.)*

This large, bushy shrub rarely grows higher than 3 m. The pith of its young twigs is cinnamon-coloured. Its leaves are like those of *S. nigra (q. v.)*, but with shiny, narrowly lanceolate leaflets, the terminal one either the same size or rather smaller than the others. (For description of genus see p. 37) The small, 5-petalled flowers are greenish-white and carried in dense ovoid clusters at the branch terminals. The mature drupe is round and fleshy, and bright scarlet. This species is found in the highlands of Rhodopi in Thrace, and the mountains of Arcadia in the Peloponnese.

Another type of elder found in Greece is the dwarf **Danewort** *(S. ebulus)*, which has perennial roots but throws up annual branches which grow to 1 m or so.

## Viburnums

### 189. Laurustinus *(Viburnum tinus L.)*

This evergreen shrub grows 2-3 m high, with pointed oval leaves 5-8

**1, 2** *Black elder*　　**3** *Red-berried elder*　　**4, 5** *Laurustinus*

cm long, on short petioles, glossily deep green above and lighter green on the underside, where they are tufted with hair in the axils of the veins. The small white flowers, opening from pink buds, grow in dense, slightly domed umbels from the branch terminals. (For description of genus see p. 37) The fruit is a drupe, metallic blue when fully ripe. Laurustinus grows in scrubland on mountain slopes in Epirus, on Corfu, Crete, Mytilene (Lesbos), and elsewhere.

### 190. Wayfaring tree *(Viburnum lantana* L.)

Despite its designation as a tree, this deciduous species grows as a shrub, no higher than 5 m. It has wrinkled, elliptically oblong leaves, 5-10 cm long and downy on the underside. The tube of the flower corolla (for description of genus see p. 37) is only half as long as the petal-lobes, and the white flowers making up the dense terminal umbels are all the same size. The fleshy drupes change from bright red to black as they ripen. Wayfaring tree is to be found in mountain locations all over mainland Greece.

### 191. Guelder rose *(Viburnum opulus* L.)

This low deciduous shrub reaches only 2-4 m in height. The leaves (for description of genus see p. 37) are usually quite deeply divided into 3 dentate lobes. They are carried on long petioles, and in autumn turn a beautiful shade of red. The white flowers are massed in lax, flat umbels at the branch terminals. They are very unequal in size: the female flowers resemble those of *V. tinus (q. v.)* above, the males on the outer perimeter of the umbel have much larger petals, making them double the size of the females. The drupe is red and fleshy. Guelder rose grows in all the mountain forests of northern Greece. Variants with all-male flowers are cultivated for decorative purposes in parks and gardens.

## Honeysuckles

### 192. Etruscan honeysuckle *(Lonicera etrusca* Santi*)*

This is a woody shrub only 1-3 m high but with long, thin rambling branches. The opposite leaves of fleshy texture are obovate, rounded at the tip, and only the lower ones have petioles. They change from brilliant

---

**1** *Laurustinus*  **2, 3** *Wayfaring tree*  **4, 5** *Guelder rose*  **6** *Etrusca honey-suckle*

1

2                                                          X1

3

4

5    X1
     X1

6

light green to blue-green as they mature. The leaves borne higher up on the branches have their bases fused and grow all the way round the twig. The fragile-looking flowers are creamy-white, flushed with pink on the outside, and very beautifully scented. The corolla tube divides into two petal-lobes, the lower one narrow and drooping, the other broad, upright, deeply serrated into four sections curved slightly backwards. Long yellow stamens protrude from the corolla throat. The flowers grow in clusters of about 6 at the tip of a long common stalk from where the fused leaves emerge. The seeds are bright red drupes growing in tight clusters. Etruscan honeysuckle is found in bushland and forests in the highland belt throughout Greece. (For description of genus see p. 38)

### 193. Common honeysuckle *(Lonicera periclymenum* L.*)*

This robust shrub grows up to 6 m high but is very similar to Etruscan honeysuckle above *(q. v.)*, except that the higher leaves remain separate and do not fuse. The flowers, similar to those of *L. etrusca*, grow without petioles. They are faintly downy, and again creamy-yellow, often flushed with pink. Common honeysuckle is very widespread from northern Greece and Macedonia to Corfu. (For description of genus see p. 38)

### 194. Fly honeysuckle *(Lonicera xylosteum* L.*)*

The branches of this 1-3 m high species are rather more upright. The opposite oval to elliptical leaves have long petioles and are fairly downy on the underside. The flowers are smaller than those of the two species described above *(q. v.)*, but have the same individual structure. Creamy-yellow, they are hairy on the outer surface, and grow in twos on top of a single stem from the leaf axils. The paired fruits are fleshy red drupes, lightly attached but not actually fused. Fly honeysuckle grows in the mountains of northern Greece. (For description of genus see p. 38)

### 195. Greek honeysuckle *(Lonicera hellenica* Orph.*)*

This 1-3 m high shrub has very slim and tender branches, downy as well as glandular. The opposite leaves are oval, hairy above and densely velvety on the underside. The typical honeysuckle flowers (see Etruscan honeysuckle above and description of genus p. 38) grow in twos on the tip

---

**1, 2** *Etruscan honeysuckle*     **3** *Common honeysuckle*     **4, 5** *Fly honeysuckle*
**6** *Greek honeysuckle*

of a long, common stalk from the leaf axils, and are a deep pink. The fruits are as described for *L. xylosteum (q. v.)*, This species grows on Mt Helmos in Thrace and in the Peloponnese.

Greece also has several dwarf honeysuckles, which only grow to about 1 m in height: **Field honeysuckle** *(L. implexa)*, with creeping or rambling shoots and a whitish-yellow flower tinged lightly with pink on the outside; **Perfoliate honeysuckle** *(L. caprifolium)*, similar to *L. implexa;* **Alpine honeysuckle** *(L. alpigena)*, with pink flowers and rather upright shoots, whose paired fruits are joined together in a large, red, fleshy structure the size of a cherry; and **Rock honeysuckle** *(L. numularifolia)*, with ovoid disc-shaped leaves and pink flowers on upright or spreading branches.

# Palm

*The palm was the traditional birth tree of Egypt, Babylonia, Arabia and Phoenicia. Its connection with birth came about from its growing near the sea, universal birth symbol, since without salt at their roots young palms grow stunted. Palms were sacred to foam-born Aphrodite, and the Tree of Life in the Babylonian Garden of Eden story is a palm. Its name devolved to that of the phoenix bird which was said to nest in its branches.*

### 196. Cretan palm *(Phoenix theophrastii)*

This tall tree has almost the same appearance as the date, and grows self-propagated exclusively on Crete. It attains a height of about 15 m, and has a very round, unbranched trunk. The largest stand of palms is found on the beach at Vai on the eastern tip of Crete. Palm leaves are pinnately compound, up to 2 m long, and the individual folioles grow on either side of a hard, very thick central rib. The leaves emerge one closely above the other directly from the top of the trunk, and droop downwards under their own weight. The small flowers hang massed in very large bunches, which are at first enclosed in a large membraneous sheath which then splits open. The fruit resembles the date in form, and hangs in densely-branched bunches with long, central stalks. (For description of genus see p. 38).

## Chamaerops

### 197. Dwarf fan-palm *(Chamaerops humilis)*

This dwarf species of palm does not exceed 2 m in height. The

**1** *Greek honeysuckle*   **2** *Cretan palm*   **3** *Dwarf fan-palm*

3

compound leaves are palmate and deeply fringed into very many folioles. They again emerge straight from the trunk, as in Cretan palm above (q. v.). The flowers and fruits also similar to those of Cretan palm and date palm respectively; the fruit is tart, however, and hard. Dwarf fan-palm can be found self-propagated in several locations on Crete. (For description of genus see p. 38).

# Tamarisk

### 198. Smyrna tamarisk (*Tamarix smyrnensis* Bunge)

This low tree or shrub has reddish branches with very small greyish green leaves, lanceolate or oval in shape. (For description of genus see p. 38) The little pinkish flowers appear in August and form large compound clusters at the branch terminals; each cluster consists of smaller clusters of up to 4 cm in length. Smyrna tamarisk grows freely in southern Greece and the Peloponnese, close to the sea or in swampy areas.

### 199. Pallas tamarisk (*T. pallasii* Desv.)

This species is in all respects similar to the above (q.v.), but the flowers tend to be a more brownish pink. Both the main cluster and the component clusters are a little larger than those of Smyrna tamarisk. This subspecies also grows by the sea anywhere in Greece. (For description of genus see p. 38)

### 200. Cretan tamarisk (*Tamarix cretica* Bunge)

The leaves of this small tree or shrub are bright green. The little pink flowers grow not only in dense clusters at the branch terminals, but also along the whole length of the branch. Cretan tamarisk is found on river banks and ravines in Crete. (For description of genus see p. 38).

**1** *Dwarf fan-palm*  **2, 3** *Smyrna tamarisk*  **4** *Pallas tamarisk*  **5** *Cretan tamarisk*

# GLOSSARY OF BOTANICAL TERMS

| | |
|---|---|
| **alternate** | (leaves) set at intervals on opposing sides of the twig |
| **anther** | top part of stamen *(q.v.)* containing pollen |
| **axillary** | of flowers growing in the leaf axils |
| **bole** | trunk of a tree |
| **bract, bracteole** | small or very small leaf or scale |
| **calyx** | whorl of sepals *(q.v.)*, often joined in a tube at the base, forming outer case of flower |
| **capsule** | dry fruit formed by two or more fused carpels *(q.v.)* which splits open when ripe |
| **carpel** | individual section of fruit |
| **catkin** | crowded spike of tiny flowers, usually hanging like a tassel |
| **compound** | (leaves) formed of several leaflets or folioles together on a common stalk |
| **cone** | rounded or elongated structure composed of layered overlapping scales *(q.v.)* bearing pollen in flower cones, and seeds when mature |
| **coniferous** | cone-bearing |
| **corolla** | collective whorl of petals, separate or fused at the base into a coralla tube |
| **corymb** | erect raceme *(q.v.)* with lower flower stalks proportionately longer |
| **cruciform** | cross-shaped flower with four equal petals |
| **cupule** | cup-shaped receptacle around seeds |
| **deciduous** | shedding its leaves in winter |
| **dentate** | with tooth-like notches |
| **drupe** | fleshy or pulpy fruit containing stone |
| **evergreen** | not shedding its leaves regularly every twelve months |
| **foliole** | one of the constituents of a compound *(q.v.)* leaf; a leaflet |
| **genus** | botanical category comprising several species |
| **glabrous** | free from hair |
| **glandular** | having glands, i.e. excreting cells, on the surface |
| **haw** | fruit of the genus Hawthorn |
| **hip** | fruit of the genus Rose |
| **hybrid** | cross-bred |

| | |
|---|---|
| **inferior** | of ovary *(q.v.)* situated below the other organs of the flower |
| **key** | large leafy bract *(q.v.)* on leaf stalk |
| **lanceolate** | lance-shaped |
| **legume** | fruit pod of the genus *Leguminosae* (p. 29) which splits down its length and contains several seeds in a row |
| **leguminous** | of or like the botanical family of *Leguminosae,* with flowers like those of the sweet pea (see p. 29) |
| **lenticels** | breathing pores in the bark of trees |
| **linear** | needle-shaped |
| **lobed** | dividing into projecting sections |
| **maquis** | mediterranean vegetation of intermingled green shrubs and trees |
| **obovate** | inverted ovate or egg-shaped, having broadest part at the tip |
| **ovary** | fertile part of female flower containing ovules which ripen into seeds, and usually one or more styles and stigmata |
| **ovate** | egg-shaped, with broadest part at the base |
| **ovoid** | oval, with one end more pointed than the other |
| **paired** | of leaves, set two opposite each other at intervals up the twig |
| **palmate** | spreading like the fingers of the hand |
| **petiole** | leaf stalk |
| **pinnate** | spreading like a feather |
| **pistil** | female flower organ, consisting of ovary *(q.v.)* upward projecting style *(q.v.)* and stigma *(q.v.)* |
| **pubescent** | covered with downy hair |
| **raceme** | flower cluster with separate flowers attached by short stalks at equal distances along cental stem |
| **radial** | of flowers: the petals arranged like rays or radii |
| **recurved** | bent backwards |
| **rhomboidal** | approximating to the shape of a rhomb, i.e. of an oblique equilateral parallelogram, diamond or lozenge |
| **scale** | dry, thin flap of tissue, usually a modified or degenerate leaf |
| **sepals** | leaves forming the calyx *(q.v.)* |
| **serrated** | notched like a saw |
| **simple** | of leaves with continuous outline, e.g. heart-shaped, oval not lobed *(q.v.)* |
| **species** | a subdivision of a genus *(q.v.)* |

| spiny | with narrow, hard and pointed thorns or prickles |
|---|---|
| **sphenoid** | wedge-shaped |
| **stamen** | male organ of flower consisting of a threadlike stalk bearing the pollinated anther *(q.v.)* |
| **stigma** | organ in female flower which receives the male pollen; sometimes lobed (see also **pistil**) |
| **stipula** | small leaf-like appendage to leaf, usually at the base of the leaf-stem |
| **style** | a more or less elongated projection from the ovary, bearing the stigma (see also **pistil**) |
| **superior** | of ovary *(q.v.)* with its origin on the receptacle above the other parts of the flower or adjacent to the stamens |
| **trifoliate** | compound leaf consisting of 3 separate leaflets connected to the leaf stalk at a central point |
| **umbel** | flower cluster with stalks spreading from the main stem like the spokes of an umbrella |
| **umbelliferous** | with flowers borne in umbels *(q.v.)* |
| **whole** | of leaf margin when entire, not toothed in any way |

# LATIN INDEX

# INDEX OF ENGLISH AND MODERN GREEK NAMES

# BIBLIOGRAPHY

| | |
|---|---|
| Arbres et arbustes des parcs et des jardins | Runo Lowenmo |
| Dendra ke thamni | D. Voliotis N. Athanasiadis |
| Flowering shrubs | J. Pokorny |
| Flowers of Europe | Oleg Polunin |
| Flowers of Greece | A. Huxley W. Taylor |
| Flowers of Greece | G. Sfikas |
| Flowers of the Mediterranean | O. Polunin A. Huxley |
| Helliniki hloris A | H. Diapoulis |
| Trees and bushes of Europe | O. Polunin |
| Votanikon & Phytologhikon lexikon | D. Kavvadas |
| Wild flowers | M. Skytte Christiansen |
| Wild flowers of Britain and Northern Europe | R. Fitter A. Fitter M. Blamey |
| Wild flowers of Greece | C. Goulimis |

Note: *Much of the material on ancient tree lore here is based on Robert Graves'* The White Goddess.
*E.S.*